Agriculture in England
A survey of farming, 1870–1947

Jonathan Brown

Agriculture in England

A survey of farming, 1870–1947

Manchester University Press

Copyright © Jonathan Brown 1987
Published by Manchester University Press
Oxford Road, Manchester, M13 9PL, U.K.
27 South Main Street, Wolfeboro, N.H. 03894–2069, U.S.A.

British Library cataloguing in publication data
Brown, Jonathan
  Agriculture in England, 1870–1947.
  1. Agriculture—Economic aspects—
  England—History
  I. Title
  338.1'0942   HD1930.E5

Library of Congress cataloging in publication data applied for

ISBN 0–7190–1759–9 *hardback*

*Photoset in Century Schoolbook
by Northern Phototypesetting Co., Bolton
Printed in Great Britain
by Billing & Sons Limited, Worcester.*

Contents

List of tables

List of figures

vii

Preface

Agriculture, like other human activities, has had its ups and downs, its periods of confidence and prosperity, its times of distress. The middle decades of the nineteenth century were regarded as a golden age, when British farmers gloried in the task of providing food for the 'workshop of the world'. Prices of agricultural products rose, giving farmers and landlords the confidence to invest heavily in underdrainage, in new buildings, new types of farm tools and machinery, and steam power. This was the time when the idea of 'high farming' gained widespread popularity. Expenditure, at times lavish in amount, on drainage, equipment, fertilisers and feedingstuffs for livestock would be repaid in increased fertility in the soil and in the production of meat and corn. With the prices then ruling that meant profit to the farmer as well.

The seventy-five years covered by this book were, by contrast, predominantly a 'down' period. Prices were low and so were profits. The former confidence was dissipated, capital was hard to come by and investment was low. Innovation in techniques and equipment there was, but born less from confidence in the prosperity of farming than from a more parsimonious need at best to make productive investment, at worst just to make ends meet. At times things seemed dire – the early 1890s, for example, when one of those collecting evidence for the Royal Commission on agriculture presented a map liberally shaded black to show the parts of Essex where land was not being cultivated. The late 1920s and early 1930s were another time when barns were left to fall down, ditches were not cleared and hedges were uncut.

All was not unmitigated gloom. There were periods of upturn. Agriculture was modestly profitable during the ten years or so immediately before the First World War, and at times during the mid-1920s and late 1930s. But these times were not enough to counteract the long-term influences that were preventing agriculture from attaining any solid prosperity. Not even the exceptional profits of the First World War could give farmers the strength they needed, and before long they were caught up again in what has been described as a vicious downward spiral of recession, each new blow to their confidence further discouraging the investment on which a recovery might be based.[1]

It was international competition in the principal items of farm produce that had set the downward spiral in motion in the late 1870s, and which remained a most pervasive influence running right through the years to the beginning of the Second World War. Another major influence was the attitude of government. For most of the period the policy was to adhere to free trade and leave farmers to fend for themselves. Fitfully during the 1930s policy changed to grant agriculture some support and protection, and to encourage greater efficiency in the industry. Finally the Second World War brought complete government direction, setting the stage for continued support for farming down to the present day.

It was from these influences that much of the development of farming followed: the adaptation of techniques, of products and of business management to suit the economics and political conditions. It is this that forms the main part of the story recounted in these pages. In it the farmers are the central characters, for this is not meant to be a full account of the rural, even the agricultural world, and therefore the landowners and farm labourers have to take the supporting roles. It is also confined to the farmers of England and Wales. However, with international trade such an important factor to be reckoned with, it is impossible to isolate England and Wales entirely, and so it is that reference is often made to matters as affecting Britain or the United Kingdom where it is appropriate to do so. The general trends in farming's progress are the main concern of this short book. The details of regional changes to be found, for instance, in Edith Whetham's volume of the *Agrarian History of England* have, therefore, been largely omitted, not least to avoid unnecessary duplication.

Like any other of its size and scope, this book makes no claim to be the last word, but rather is a progress report on the historical research and knowledge of the period. It relies heavily on the work of others besides myself. In some chapters my part has been little more than to provide a commentary on other texts. In some my research contribution is dominant, while in the remainder the balance is quite even. The work of other scholars is invariably cited in the notes or bibliography. On the other hand, because of the general nature of the argument such sources as contemporary newspapers and manuscript collections make but rare appearance in the notes.

The writing of the book has been made possible by the labours over the years of countless archivists and librarians while I have gathered material, not always with a view to its being used for this work. It is by no means a work of oral history, but it has gained from conversations I have had with farmers who remember the years covered here, and in particular I am grateful to Mr Banks of Kilburn, Yorkshire and Mr Fisher of East Bridgford, Nottinghamshire. My friends at the Institute of Agricultural History, University of Reading, have offered encouragement and advice, and especially I should like to thank Sadie Ward, who read the manuscript and suggested a good number of improvements. And my parents furthered progress by working out some of the statistics and typing the manuscript.

Note

1.   Gavin McCrone, *The Economics of Subsidising Agriculture*, 1962, pp. 173–4.

1 Seasons, imports and prices

In 1879 the government appointed a Royal Commission on the Depressed Condition of the Agricultural Interest under the chairmanship of the Duke of Richmond, from which fact it is more simply known as the Richmond Commission. The weather was bad that year, as it had been for two or three years in succession, causing ruin to the crops, and prices were falling. The government came under pressure from agriculture's spokesmen in the House of Commons, led by Henry Chaplin, who sat for Mid-Lincolnshire, to do something for the farmer. One of the concerns of the Duke of Richmond's Commission was to discover the cause of the farmer's difficulties. When the final report was issued in 1882 the conclusion was that 'all the witnesses whom we have examined have agreed in ascribing it mainly to a succession of unfavourable seasons'.[1]

Fourteen years later, in 1893, another Royal Commission was appointed, with a less cumbersome title, to investigate agricultural depression. Once again the seasons were unfavourable. There was drought, causing crops to be light and cattle thin. Prices were still low. Indeed, the price of wheat fell to its lowest of the whole nineteenth century in 1894. The officially returned average was 22s 10d per quarter, but farmers widely spoke of having to sell for as little as 18s. Once again the government was called upon to do something. After slightly lengthier deliberations this second commission published its final report in 1897, where it declared that 'among all classes of agriculturists there is a consensus of opinion that the chief cause of the existing depression is the progressive and serious decline in the prices of farm produce'.[2] A longer perspective, of course, greatly influenced the change in emphasis. It was not that the witnesses of 1879 and 1880 had ignored the fall in prices. That featured well up on the list of causes of agricultural distress. But the bad seasons were more visible and immediate, hence uppermost in many people's thoughts. By 1897 the seasons had come and gone, some good, some bad, and prices had kept on falling regardless.

The weather the farmers complained of in the late 1870s was certainly bad, enough to make anyone feel depressed. They were unusually wet years. The rainfall for the years 1875 to 1882 was about 14 per cent above average. Some places came out far worse. Among the extreme records were Englefield, in Berkshire, with rainfall 35 per cent greater than average, Lincoln, with 33 per cent and Worksop, 29 per cent.[3] Of these eight years, 1879 was almost universally found to be disastrously wet, and 1880 was little better. The official reports for 1879 speak soberly in terms of the rainfall that year being 'remarkable both for its frequency and for the amount measured', but it is a fair bet that much less temperate language passed amongst the farmers around the inns on market day.[4] Central and eastern districts suffered most from the excess rain. For the year November 1878 to October 1879 Bury St. Edmunds received 12·13 in. more rain than usual, 51 per cent above average, whereas Maidstone reported an extra 3·7 in. (15 per cent above average), and York only 1·5 in. (5 per cent above average).[5] It was not the total fall of rain alone that caused problems, but its distribution throughout the year. In both 1879 and 1880 certain seasons were particularly wet, with the result that much of the work of those periods

2

was ruined. In 1879 rainfall was over four inches greater than normal in both spring and summer, the growing and ripening seasons.[6] In 1880 the wet seasons were summer and autumn. There were serious floods in the fens, and everywhere the harvest was disrupted, with crops sometimes not cut until December.

The effect of the weather on the crops was disastrous. The yields of cereals in 1879 were widely reported to be no more than three-quarters, often as little as half, the average for the years from about 1873 to 1877 (table 1). The harvest of 1880 was about as bad, although in some parts of the country farmers escaped quite lightly. In Cornwall, where crops in 1879 had done better than in most other places, the 1880 harvest was reckoned to be 'exceptionally good'.[7] In both years wheat produced the worst results.

Table 1 Yields of wheat in the 1870s (*quarters per acre*)

	Average before 1878	*1878*	*1879*
Berkshire, Benham estate	4	3	2½
Surrey, Clandon estate	3	4	3¼
Kent, West Ashford Union	4	4	2
Bedfordshire	4	3	2
Essex, Chelmsford Union	4	2	1½
Northamptonshire, Brixworth Union	4	3½	2½
Leicestershire	4	2½	1½
Yorkshire, Holderness	4¾	3¾	2
Yorkshire, Pocklington Union	3	3	1¼
Cumberland, Penrith Union	2½	2¼	1⅞
Lancashire	4¼	4¼	3¾

Source. RC Agriculture 1879, Reports of Assistant Commissioners.

Barley generally yielded poor crops, but there were farmers who succeeded in getting reasonable crops, if not quite a full yield. The results from oats, however, were considerably better, in not a few places well up to an average yield. The quality of the crops was rarely up to standard. Rain-sodden wheat was of limited value for milling, and the Richmond Commission was presented with a succession of tales of farmers having to feed most of their wheat to livestock. What they were able to sell was usually light, no more than 55–58 lb to the bushel compared with the normal weight of 63 lb. Barley growers likewise found it more difficult to interest maltsters in their crop.

The sufferings of arable farming as a result of the wet seasons were particularly striking. It was, after all, the main grain-growing counties of the Midlands, central southern England and East Anglia that experienced the most abnormal rainfall. But livestock farming, too, had its problems. Grass grew abundantly, of course, but often pastures were waterlogged and hay was cut in poor condition so that the animals derived little benefit. Even more perversely, in 1880 a dry spring retarded the growth of the meadows, and then the rain fell during haymaking. Consequently graziers were regularly reporting that their stock were underweight and out of condition.

Those problems were as nothing compared to the effects of serious outbreaks of disease in animals. Wet pastures proved ideal conditions for the spread of some of the sheep's worst afflictions. One was a bacterial condition affecting the feet and ankles, and known as foot rot. The second was the work of a parasite which attacked the liver, with debilitating effect. It was a condition known as liver rot, or, more accurately, liver fluke. There were outbreaks of both diseases, but it was the fluke that did the most damage, carrying off nearly a tenth of the nation's sheep in two years. It was not unusual for farmers to have entire flocks wiped out. Again, those in the unusually wet Midlands were among the greatest sufferers. In Leicestershire the number of sheep in 1881 was as much as 37 per cent less than it had been in 1878 before these troubles started. In Rutland the decline was 20 per cent, in Oxfordshire 22 per cent, these in comparison with losses of but 8 per cent in Durham and Sussex, and 2 per cent in Kent. Several western districts were among the heavy losers – Somerset, for example, where the flock was reduced by 28 per cent, and most of the Welsh counties recorded losses above average.

As if those losses were not enough, cattle also fell prey, first, to pleuro-pneumonia in 1879, then to foot-and-mouth disease, which first became serious during 1880 and 1881 in eastern England. The outbreaks persisted, not declining until late in 1883, and spread throughout the country. Farmers did not have their herds decimated in the way their flocks had been. Compulsory slaughter was not then the official policy for controlling the spread of foot-and-mouth, and as it was a disease from which animals could recover farmers generally allowed it to run its course. Their animals were less healthy, less useful for breeding, and of less value in the market, but even a reduced price was better than nothing. That was assuming the farmer could get to market, since the government's principal measure to contain the spread of infection was to order the closure of markets and fairs. With such a long-lasting epidemic, there were markets kept closed for months on end, especially in the worst-affected eastern counties. It was extremely troublesome for farmers, and by late 1883 they were making their frustrations known through petitions to the Privy Council asking for local markets to be reopened.

With low yields and a major outbreak of disease directly attributable to the exceptionally bad weather of 1879 and 1880 it was only natural that people should see this as being at the heart of farming's difficulties. A steady procession of land agents, leading farmers and other agricultural

5

specialists, among them some of the most eminent, came before the Richmond Commission and declared it to be so. Landowners stood up at rent audit dinners and told the tenantry that they had bad seasons to blame for their troubles, repeating the theme at meetings of the agricultural societies and the chambers of agriculture. The local papers in rural areas had their correspondence columns filled with letters from 'Agricola' and similarly anonymous writers giving their support to this view. It followed that the depression must be short-lived. As soon as the sun again began to shine at the right seasons prosperity would return. Thus it was that when the weather was reasonable in the early summer of 1880 the speeches at agricultural meetings and the columns of the rural press were filled with such sentiments as the editorial of the *Retford News* in June: 'Agricultural prospects are improving . . . the agricultural classes and political economists may venture to hope that the farming troubles of the past years are over, and long looked-for "better times" are reached at last'.[8]

It is easy to see now that such optimism was misguided. There were some at the time who thought so. James Banks Stanhope, owner of the Revesby Abbey estate in Lincolnshire, told the Richmond Commission that he expected the return of normal seasons to do no more than enable farmers to survive rather than earn healthy profits. It was not long before the optimists began to change their views. After 1881 the seasons did return to normal. Harvests through the 1880s and 1890s, if a little on the low side of the official average, were generally reasonable. The main exceptions were three years in the early 1890s when the weather again upset things. The wheat crop of 1892 was deficient because its growing season was shortened by wet weather delaying sowing the previous autumn. Then followed two years when spring and early summer were exceptionally dry. Cereal yields were low, but variable. Farmers in some districts suffered little loss while those maybe not far away found their corn well below average. It was the livestock farmer who suffered most from these seasons. Crops of hay and roots were deficient, leaving farmers short of feed. Graziers had to sell stock well below their usual weight. There were dairy farmers who had to reduce the size of their herds because they could not feed the full complement. Even at their worst, though, these seasons were not as disastrous as the late 1870s, and farmers had them in better perspective. The real burden of the grazier's complaint was that prices for fatstock had fallen quite sharply over four or five years. The arable farmer's main concern was the decline of corn prices to their lowest yet recorded. The official average for wheat in 1893 was 22s 10d a quarter, but sales for as low as 18s were regularly reported from eastern county markets, a price at which many farmers decided their corn was better used as cattle feed. Low prices had assumed first place among most people's assessments of the causes of depression during the preceding ten years. As more normal weather and harvests returned during the 1880s without the expected return to prosperity, so one by one those involved in agriculture changed their views, from the humblest tenant farmer to Henry Chaplin, the leading spokesman in Parliament for arable farming interests, who told members of an agricultural society in 1884 that the good season had forced him to conclude that the 'real cause of agricultural depression at the present time is the bad prices you receive for the staple of your produce'.[9]

The final quarter of the nineteenth century was a time when prices generally were falling. Between 1871–75 and 1894–98 prices fell by an average of about forty per cent, but, as table 2 shows, some agricultural prices fell considerably more than the average. Wheat prices fell the furthest, by some 51 per cent. Being the main bread grain, wheat had traditionally played the role of barometer of agricultural prosperity, so it is hardly surprising that a fall in prices

Table 2 Changes in price of principal agricultural
commodities, 1871–75 to 1894–98 (%)

	Average decrease
Wheat	51
Wool	50
Potatoes	39
Barley	39
Oats	38
Pork	33
Beef	29
Butter	25
Mutton	25

Source. W. T. Layton and G. Crowther, *An Introduction to the Study of Prices* (2nd ed., 1935), p. 88.

on this scale should provoke considerable outcry. The other cereals also fell heavily, but the greater decline of wheat destroyed established differentials and made barley or oats a better prospect for many farmers. In the early 1890s the average price for barley at eastern county markets was often higher than wheat, and the premium for good malting samples made barley's position even more favourable.

Only wool prices fell by as much as did wheat. They had started to fall in the 1860s, and between 1871–75 and 1891–95 came down by almost 50 per cent. Other livestock products, by contrast, fell in price far less than the average. The price of meat in the 1890s was generally no more than one-third lower than it had been in the 1870s, with the higher quality products maintaining their prices the better. That in turn kept the prices paid to breeders for store cattle from falling so disastrously. Prices for store cattle in Welsh markets fell by 20 per cent between 1877–80 and 1894–97, and for store ewes the decline was only 6 per cent. Fat cattle and sheep prices in these markets fell by 19 per cent and 18 per cent respectively.[10] Butter and cheese, after falling sharply in price in the late 1870s, recovered during the following decade, so that for the period to the early 1890s the average price of cheese was 30 per cent lower, that of butter 16 per cent. Milk prices remained more or less steady, while eggs actually rose.

With such a wide divergence between the prices of different commodities there was clearly more affecting agricultural markets than the general deflationary movements in the economy as a whole. The factor which came to have greatest prominence in contemporary discussions was foreign competition. Agriculture had been expanding in new territories overseas, in North and South America, Australasia and India. With simultaneous improvements in transport there was emerging by the 1870s an effective world economy in some of the principal products of farming, and that immeasurably increased the supply of food available to Britain – indeed, to all the countries of western Europe. Wheat grown at low cost on the prairies could travel over the continental railroads and in transatlantic steamships so cheaply that it could be sold in London for less than the harvest of East Anglia. British farmers cried foul, suspecting international merchants, shipping lines and railway companies at home of devious dealings.[11] The facts of international trade were against them. By 1879 the *Economist*'s assessment of the corn trade was: 'The home production of corn is not the over-ruling power in the land which it once was . . . corn factors are accustomed to look as much to the "visible supply" in the United States as to the harvest returns here'.[12]

It was in the market for cereals that foreign competition first became effective. Imports of corn were, of course, no novelty. It was more than a century since Britain had been self-sufficient in wheat. By the 1850s about a quarter of the nation's supply of wheat was imported, and the proportion rose to 50 per cent by 1873–75. These imports were large enough to depress the price of wheat at home, for prices

9

were lower in the early 1870s than they had been in the early 1850s. The downward movement had passed little noticed, however, because it was gentle and because there were enough years with prices of 55s–65s a quarter to make wheat appear to be a prosperous crop. While wheat was slipping in price, barley and oats, which were not imported on any scale, rose by about 25 and 15 per cent between the early 1850s and 1870s.

In the later 1870s overseas supplies began seriously to undercut the British market. In 1879 imports of wheat rose by nearly 10 million cwt to 59·5 million cwt, an enormous change for one year. Certainly these shipments were making up for the deficiencies in the British harvest, but they were coming in so cheaply that prices were falling when in previous years of poor crops they would have risen. Farmers felt cheated of their compensation in the market place for disappointment in the harvest field, and they complained voluminously. Sir James Caird gave statistical support to farmers' memories when he demonstrated that for five poor years in the period 1853–62 when the yield of wheat averaged only twenty-four bushels per acre the price was 61s 6d, whereas for five similar years in the 1870s the price had fallen to 49s 10d for crops averaging nineteen bushels per acre.[13]

It was the farmers' great misfortune that a run of bad seasons in England and the growing strength of overseas competition should have come together as they did. For one thing, the enormous increase in shipments of wheat between 1878 and 1880, making good the deficiencies of the home harvests, gave foreign wheat a dominant share of the British market more quickly than might otherwise have happened. Imports accounted for 60 per cent of wheat supplies in 1878–80. By 1891–93 the proportion was 71 per cent. A second consequence was that agriculturalists were misled into thinking foreign competition less severe than it proved to be. All members of the farming interest fell prey to this. In estate archives there are plenty of letters and memoranda passed between landowners' agents and farmers assuring each other that once there was a normal harvest imports would return to manageable proportions. Several of those prominent in farming life nationally or locally stated such opinions publicly. In a paper presented to the Royal Statistical Society, Thomas Brassey declared that the intensity of American competition should be reduced because the costs of production and transport would rise as new lands entered their 'second generation' of cultivation. Sir James Caird offered similar views to the Richmond Commission, while Albert Pell, just returned from a study tour of the United States, expressed another oft repeated view, that meat producers had little to fear from overseas.[14]

Such determined optimism proved to be unfounded. Wheat imports continued to grow in quantity. So did barley, doubling between 1870–74 and 1890–94 as malt-sters bought more of their cheaper sorts from places as far apart as California and Asia Minor. Imports of wool, mainly from Australia and New Zealand, also nearly doubled in volume, from 200 million lb in 1874 to 370 million lb in 1895. Imports were already taking over the British market in the 1870s, accounting for 59·2 per cent in 1876–78; by 1893–95 it had become 73·6 per cent.[15] What confounded people like Mr Pell, though, was the rise in imports of meat. They, too, doubled in volume between the 1870s and 1890s, but most of the increase came after 1882. The introduction of chilling and refrigeration played an important part, allowing supplies to be shipped the 12,000 miles from Australia and New Zealand, and to arrive in better condition than much of the salted and tinned meat previously imported. The new techniques of preserving were mainly responsible for the huge increase in the imports of dead meat from 133,890 tons a year in 1870–74 to 351,890 tons a year in 1885–89. Live animals continued to be brought in in

11

increasing numbers, but their share of total meat imports was down to less than a quarter by 1885.[16] Concern to restrict the spread of foot-and-mouth and other epidemic diseases caused the government to place restrictions on imports of livestock, culminating in prohibition under the Diseases of Animals Act of 1896.

'When comparing the imports of livestock and meat for different periods of the last twenty years, the wonder is that prices have kept up as well as they have,' wrote W. E. Bear in 1891.[17] The truth was, however, that the foreign supplies of meat came far less as competition than as a complement to home supplies. Demand for meat in Britain was rising more quickly than the country's farmers could increase production. Consumption was greater by more than a million tons in 1910–14 compared with 1870–74, this a result of a population increasing not only in numbers but also in wealth, and turning to a diet less dependent on the bread grains. Hence it was that while imports in 1895 took a share of the market for beef amounting to 28·4 per cent, 31·4 per cent for mutton and as high as 48·8 per cent for pork, prices moved roughly in line with the average for the economy as a whole.[18]

Those trends in the markets also help explain why it was that the assistant commissioners touring the country on behalf of the Duke of Richmond's Commission had rather little in the nature of agricultural depression to report from northern and western counties, where livestock formed the mainstay of farming. Things were different when the next Royal Commission investigated, for the imports of frozen meat had made an impression, and the dry weather of recent years had made life particularly difficult for livestock farmers by restricting the supplies of fodder. Even so, the trends were clear. Demand, prices and therefore profits were firmer in the livestock trade than they were for the cereal farmer. The wet seasons of the late 1870s had obscured those trends. The tragedy was that by the time the seasons had returned to normal and it was realised just how the markets were changing, for many an arable farmer it had become too late.

Notes

1. R C Agricultural Interest, Final Report, pp. 12–13.
2. RC Agriculture 1893, Final Report, p. 43.
3. G. J. Symons, 'Recent British weather', *Journal of the Royal Agricultural Society of England,* xliv, 1883, pp. 416–21.
4. *Journal of the Royal Agricultural Society of England,* xl, 1879, p. 111.
5. J. C. Morton, 'The past agricultural year', *Journal of the Royal Agricultural Society of England,* xli, 1880, p. 215.
6. The records from Greenwich Observatory for the second and third quarters of 1879 showed rainfall 4·4 and 4·5 in. above normal. *Journal of the Royal Agricultural Society of England,* xli, 1880, pp. i–x.
7. RC Agricultural Interest 1879, Report of Mr Little on the Southern Counties, p. 11.
8. *Retford News,* 26 June 1880. *Agricultural Gazette,* 4 October 1880.
9. *Stamford Mercury,* 21 November 1884.
10. David Howell, *Land and People in Nineteenth Century Wales,* 1978, pp. 8–9.
11. The unfairness of foreign competition was demonstrated by the following exchange during the proceedings of the Richmond Commission: '(The President) I suppose that a ton of English wheat represents very much the same weight as a ton of foreign wheat? – Yes.' Clearly, foreigners would stoop to anything to reach the British market. RC Agricultural Distress 1879, q. 7962.
12. *Economist,* 5 July 1879.
13. RC Agricultural Interest 1879, q. 62647.
14. Thomas Brassey, 'Agriculture in England and the United States', *Journal of the Royal Statistical Society,* xlii, 1879, p. 763. RC Agricultural Interst 1879, qq. 22649–52, 22818–19, 56394–8, 62658.
15. *Board of Trade, Annual Statement of Trade.* RC Agriculture 1893, Final Report, p. 74.
16. Richard Perren, *The Meat Trade in Britain, 1840–1914,* 1978, pp. 123–4. J. T. Critchell and R. Raymond, *A History of the Frozen Meat Trade,* 1912.
17. W. E. Bear, 'The future of agricultural competition', *Journal of the Royal Agricultural Society of England,* lii, 1891, p. 760.
18. RC Agriculture 1893, Final Report, p. 65. Richard Perren, *The Meat Trade in Britain, 1840–1914,* 1978, pp. 3, 106.

2 The finances of farming 1870–1914

One of the ill effects of the years from 1878 to 1881 was a series of financial losses that hindered farming's progress for some time to come. Poor yields and low prices combined to push farmers' accounts into deficit. The Richmond Commission collected dozens of sample farm accounts showing losses of £1–£2, sometimes £3 an acre. There was the farm of 221 acres in Warwickshire where the loss was £640 on a capital of £2,000 in 1878–79. Of two farms on the Yorkshire wolds, one, of 275 acres, lost £487; the other, of 745 acres, lost £671. A farm of 400 acres in Kent lost £754 in 1879 and another £521 in 1880. These were all examples of arable and mixed farms. The healthier state of livestock farming is indicated by the almost complete absence of samples collected from the western counties of England and Wales. The assistant commissioner in Cumberland really had nothing to report by way of loss-making farms. In some of the dairying districts of Wiltshire, Somerset and Dorset, for example, there was considerably more distress in 1879 and 1880, when imports of cheese undermined the market.[1]

Heavy losses drained farmers' capital and reserves. This again was a common theme among evidence collected by the Richmond Commission, although expressed usually in general terms, as by the Essex farmer who said he had lost 30–50 per cent of his capital in six years. Sir James Caird tried to calculate how much capital had been lost in British farming in the six years to 1880, and came up with the total of £139 million.[2] The effects of the losses of the 1870s were to be felt throughout the 1880s and '90s. For, although profits were to be made during the 1880s, they were often modest and did little to recoup the earlier losses. Indeed, as contemporaries were quick to point out, with inadequate allowance made for interest on capital and management charges, by the standards of most other businesses the farmers' returns were negligible. Profits were by no means certain during the 1880s, the odd year of loss that intervened merely adding to farmers' problems. In the arable and mixed farming districts farmers continued to complain that they were paying their rents out of pocket. At the audits the estate agent was faced with a procession of tenants asking for a few weeks' grace while they sold a stack of corn or flock of sheep which would enable them to pay the rent. Such weak recovery from the losses of 1879 made farming ill equipped to withstand a further few years when losses reached similar proportions in the early 1890s. This time there was greater hardship in the livestock counties, but because farmers here were even more reluctant than most to keep accounts there is little substantial information beyond such general statements to the Royal Commission as the north Devon farmer's claim to have lost half a year's rent in 1893. The Royal Commission collected more accounts from the southern and eastern parts of the country, from which it is possible to get some small indication of the course of profits and losses (table 3).

The impression to be gained from these facts is that farming was seriously undercapitalised throughout the Great Depression. It is a view with which contemporaries concurred. In surveys such as the one carried out by W. E. Bear in the early 1890s insufficient capital was the most common cause of farming failure cited by farmers and

Table 3 Profits and losses on three farms in eastern England, 1876–94: (a) Yorkshire, farm of 837 acres (757 acres arable)

	Profit			Loss		
	£	s	d	£	s	d
1879				369	7	0½
1880				157	4	1
1881	36	8	10½			
1882	226	16	8½			
1883				100	3	9
1884	284	11	11			
1885	456	5	2			
1886				235	14	1
1887				102	9	6
1888				536	10	8
1889				253	2	11
1890	203	14	1			
1891	803	2	3			
1892				242	16	0
1893	41	15	0			

Source. RC Agriculture 1893, Farm Accounts, pp. 195–202.

estate agents.[3] Landowners and agents regularly complained that tenants had too little capital to farm their holdings adequately, to withstand years of loss, and, perhaps most important, to enable them to make changes in their methods of farming necessary to adapt to the prevailing markets. It was men of capital who could afford to convert arable to pasture, and who could then afford to buy the cattle to stock the land.

It was not an entirely new theme, but one perhaps made more urgent. In an article published in 1878 E. P. Squarey, partner in one of the largest firms of estate agents in southeast England, claimed that 'as a rule, it may be accepted that tenants' capital has not flowed liberally into farming

Table 3 (*contd.*): Profits and losses on three farms in eastern England, 1876–94: (b) Lincolnshire, farm 1,800 acres near Caistor, turnip and barley land

	Profit			Loss			Capital per acre		
	£	s	d	£	s	d	£	s	d
1879–80				3736	19	0	9	18	0
1880–81				1499	0	10½	10	1	6
1881–82	512	9	9½				10	3	6
1882–83	1069	13	8				10	5	0
1883–84				80	10	9	9	12	0
1884–85	479	7	9½				9	11	0
1885–86				1392	4	3	8	12	0
1886–87				845	19	4	7	19	6
1887–88	1531	19	2½				7	10	0
1888–89				365	10	6½	7	12	6
1889–90	564	13	7				7	2	0
1890–91	659	6	7				7	9	6
1891–92				1263	14	8	6	16	0
1892–93				1432	14	6½	6	14	0
1893–94				1532	7	10	6	9	0

Source. RC Agriculture 1893, Report of A. Wilson Fox on Lincolnshire, p. 125.

investments in England, and is more or less deficient in the amount which might be profitably employed'. Two years later the *Agricultural Gazette* suggested that 'the majority have farmed during the past thirty years with insufficient capital'.[4] Ten pounds an acre was generally regarded as the minimum amount of tenant's capital for most types of farming. Squarey suggested that at least that much was going to be needed, because the new and better implements employed cost more, livestock were getting more expensive, and so was labour. Instead, he had to recognise that most tenants had no more than £6 an acre. It was not

Table 3 (*contd.*): Profits and losses on three farms in eastern England, 1876–94: (c) Hall Farm, Toft Monks, Norfolk, 243 acres

	Profit			Loss		
	£	s	d	£	s	d
1876–77	426	2	10			
1877–78				270	15	5
1878–79				136	14	1
1879–80	89	3	2¾			
1880–81	84	1	1			
1881–82				183	7	8½
1882–83	26	4	7			
1883–84				3	14	2
1884–85	192	14	11½			
1885–86				90	8	5
1886–87	42	3	11½			
1887–88				120	10	11
1888–89	119	11	7			
1889–90	238	5	0			
1890–91				84	19	0½
1891–92				131	10	4½
1892–93	161	14	7			
1893–94	182	0	11			

Source. University of Reading, Farm Accounts collection NORF 6/1/1.

merely that farmers had too little capital, but that many in the eastern and southern arable counties had directed their resources into tillage, and into wheat especially, during the early 1870s, with the result that they had insufficient reserves to carry them through the bad seasons around 1879, and no means to revise their methods in the 1880s. This was what happened, for instance, in the down country of Wiltshire.[5] The same was true in Lincolnshire, especially the light wolds and heath, in Essex, and generally in the corn counties.

Far from increasing, as E. P. Squarey wanted, tenants' capital in arable farming fell during the Great Depression. Henry Rew, reporting on Salisbury Plain to the Royal Commission of 1893, found £8 per acre regarded as an appropriate figure for the district. More generally, about £5 an acre was often quoted as the amount tenants invested in their farms in the 1900s. In some accounts it is possible to observe the process of capital reduction. One of the Royal Commission's collection, for example, from a farm of 1,800 acres near Caistor, Lincolnshire, starts out with a capital of £10 per acre which reduces by a few shillings each year to finish at £6 9s an acre in 1893 (table 3).[6] However, the reduction in farming capital was not quite as drastic as might at first appear. With lower rents and the costs of feed, fertilisers, implements and livestock generally less than they had been in the 1860s and 1870s, it was possible to farm adequately on a smaller capital investment.

For some the strain proved too much. There were nearly five times as many bankruptcies in 1881 as there had been in 1871. At 700 out of a total of 223,000 farmers in England and Wales the bankrupts hardly represent the wholesale collapse of an industry, but the fact that the numbers were so much higher does show that farmers were finding it hard to cope. The relatively easy conditions for those in the pastoral regions are borne out by the near absence of bankruptcies in Cumberland and throughout much of Wales, whereas in the rain-drenched arable claylands of Huntingdonshire and East Anglia as many as one in twenty farmers could be forced out of business. Bankruptcies reached their peak in 1881, for though the difficult years of the early 1890s brought about another increase, numbers reached only about half those of ten years previously. There were in addition, however, untold numbers of farmers who found ways of retiring more gracefully.[7]

For the majority who kept on farming there were several

ways by which they could do so. They could perhaps simply shrug off the losses and live on capital or on income from other investments while waiting for happier days in farming to return. There certainly were some who did that. Among them was a farmer in downland Wiltshire who opened his accounts to the Royal Commission of 1893. On the farm of 800 acres in the seventeen years from 1877 to 1893 he recorded losses for ten of them, including each of the four years 1878 to 1881. Some of the losses were enormous – £1,791 in 1879, for example – but all, he said, had been underwritten out of his family's private income.[8]

It was necessary to be rich, or possibly reckless, to ride out the times in that way. Most farmers had to take some definite action. They had to produce more to offset the fall in prices; they had to cut costs in line with prices; or they had to find new farming methods and products which might yield profit. Attempting to increase output in order to have more to sell at the lower price is a basic reaction in agriculture. 'The lower the price of grain the more should be attempted to be produced to meet the loss. This cannot be accomplished by stinting the land of labour,' argued the author of a letter to the *Stamford Mercury* in 1878.[9] The poor harvests of the next few years made it difficult to put such a policy into effect, but the slightness of the decline in the acreage of wheat before 1883 certainly suggests that the attempt was made. It was in the end, though, a minority line of approach. For most farmers the options were to cut costs or find new products. In practice some combination of the two was generally followed.

When it came to economising, one of the first items of expenditure to which farmers turned was rent. It was a large bill, commonly taking 15–20 per cent of all expenses in the 1870s, and was therefore an obvious target for economy measures. Furthermore, the tenant had behind him the by now universally accepted tradition that in times of difficulty he should turn first to his landlord for help. The seasons of the late 1870s soon had farmers leaning on this principle: 'the seasons have of late been so very unpropitious that I am terribly perplexed, and who am I to look to but my landlord,' was typical of the language used in letters to landlords and their agents.[10]

Disastrous harvests and low prices in the late 1870s soon had arable farmers clamouring for help with their rent. The files of correspondence in estate archives are filled with letters from tenants asking for their rents to be reduced, with varying amounts of special pleading. Agents were lucky to get through a rent audit without tenants stating bluntly that they could not continue unless rents were reduced. Some handed in their notice to quit as a means of putting extra pressure on the landlord. The landlord was very likely to respond to that type of threat and go some way towards meeting the tenant, so that the notice was withdrawn.

Landlords also believed in the principle that the estate should support farmers in difficult times rather than simply let them go to the wall. It was one of the marks of a well run estate that genuine hardship would be looked upon favourably. The owners could help with rents either by making full reductions, or by granting a rebate on the amount due. Rebates, or remissions, were in principle temporary measures. Even in times of high prices the tenant whose land had suffered from flooding or had had a particularly bad outbreak of disease in his cattle would be given a remission to tide him over. Not surprisingly, in 1879 and 1880, with opinion so much in favour of the view that agriculture's troubles were but a phase which a couple of good summers would cure, landowners preferred to offer rent remissions rather than permanent reductions. Besides, even in some of the arable heartlands of eastern England, demand for farms still seemed to be strong, so there was no point in reducing the rent for existing tenants when farms could most likely be re-let at little or no change in rent. It was only when farmers began to carry out their threats to quit and it was found that there was no queue of applicants for the vacant holding that permanent reductions of rent became a regular feature. Thus it was that the agent to the Chediston Hall estate in Suffolk was resisting the pressure to make rent reductions in 1879, but two years later, with the expected recovery not materialising, the advice offered to the landlord was 'it will be best to let the farms at any rents that can be obtained'.[11]

The result of accepting any rent offered was massive reductions in parts of eastern England. The heavy clays of Essex and Huntingdonshire proved about the most difficult to let. Mr Hunter Pringle, who investigated these areas on behalf of the Royal Commission of 1893, found some examples of farms being let almost rent-free, such as the one of 638 acres at Steeple in Essex for which the tenant had to pay just £1 a year for the five years from 1886 to 1891. Farms such as that represented the extreme, but the general movement of rents in these districts was no less remarkable. Already by 1875 reductions were becoming common, so that by the mid-1880s rents were nearly 50 per cent lower than they had been in the early 1870s. Further reductions meant that by 1893–95 they were commonly no more than a quarter to a third of what they had been twenty years previously.

There were similar changes in other arable districts. On the Wilton estate in chalkland Wiltshire tenants were requesting reductions in their rents as early as 1871, and the rental of the estate started to decline from 1873. By 1890–94 the net rents received on the estate were 45 per cent of what they had been in 1869–73. Throughout arable England rents were commonly reduced by about a third, and sometimes by anything up to 60 per cent. That was not so in the more pastoral regions. Here the downward movement started later, often not until the mid to late 1880s, and did not progress so far. In Cumberland rents generally were reduced by 15–20 per cent. In Devon reductions were of the order of 5–15 per cent, with a healthy demand for farms continuing. In Wales there were permanent reductions of up to 15 per cent, but they were not common, being confined almost entirely to the more arable districts. Elsewhere temporary remissions were usually found to be satisfactory. Sometimes there was hardly any change at all, as for example in south Lancashire, where, although there were some remissions in the 1890s, rents generally held steady and even rose slightly over the period from 1870 to 1900.[12]

The distinctions are clear. Land where the value of the product was low was little in demand. The Essex clays were so costly to cultivate that with falling prices for wheat they were being pushed to the very margin as arable land. They were almost unlettable. Indeed, one of the things that most struck Hunter Pringle on his investigations for the Royal Commission of the 1890s was the extent of land either derelict or in some rather tenuous state of cultivation. By contrast, in the pastoral zone where livestock offered a real return farms continued in demand, sometimes amounting to a land hunger. The divisions remain just as clear when one moves from the broad regions dividing the whole country to find, for example, that in Wiltshire the Marquess of Bath maintained his rental income remarkably well from the Longleat estate, a large part of which was in the dairy vale of the county, while his neighbour, the Earl of Pembroke, was receiving no real income at all from his chalkland arable estate.[13] More locally still, throughout the arable and mixed farming districts it was always the land at all difficult or expensive to cultivate, usually the hilly and the strong land, that was most out of favour and for which the rents fell most heavily.

The massive reductions in rent on arable farms could not fail to make a difference to the farmers' finances – often, in fact, the vital difference. For it was not unusual for rent's share of total expenses to fall, sometimes by as much as 50 per cent. The story was different where the farming was in better heart – on dairy farms in the west, or the successful potato, fruit and vegetable farms of the fens. Here, if anything, farmers were likely to be laying out more of their expenses in rent, but for them the burden was of lesser concern.

The next major item of expenditure was labour. About a fifth of total expenses was a common proportion on medium-to-large mixed farms. For those small farmers who had to hire labour in addition to that of their families the expenditure could account for a third or more of their total costs. This was, moreover, an expense which had been growing during the 1860s and early 1870s, when times had been good. The farm labourer's wages had been rising rapidly. An index of wages in England and Wales calculated by Wilson Fox in 1903 moved from 100 in 1871 to 113·6 in 1876. The increase was greatest (17 per cent) in the northern counties, always a district of relatively high wages, and least (10 per cent) in the southern and southwestern.[14] This was the time when the new agricultural labourers' unions were at their most active. There were numerous strikes throughout the country following which farmers often agreed to pay an additional 3d or 6d a day. But they were not the only influence, for even after the long strike and lock-out in the eastern counties which ended in defeat for the National Agricultural Labourers' Union in 1873–74 wages continued to rise. Men had been leaving the land in such numbers that labour was in short supply, inducing farmers and landlords not only to pay higher wages but to increase allowances such as coal and potatoes, and to provide better cottages.[15]

When prices began to fall in the second half of the 1870s farmers were quick to declare that all should share in carrying farming through difficult times and that wages should therefore be cut. The pressure was greatest from the corn growers of the eastern counties, and by 1880 they had already succeeded in removing the sixpence a day gained during the heyday of the labourers' unions. Wages continued to move downwards in eastern England during the 1880s, to fall well below those paid in the early 1870s. The average for this region calculated by Wilson Fox was 11s 6¼d a week in 1871, falling to 10s 8d, a low point reached in 1888. In no other region were wages reduced to such an extent. In most other parts of England they fell more slowly and slightly, remaining higher throughout the 1880s than they had been in 1871. In the southern and south-western counties they continued to move gently upwards.

The second means of reducing the bill for labour was to employ less of it. The more penny-pinching ways of doing this attracted a lot of attention. Hedges were left uncut, ditches not cleared. Farmers were more strict about laying men off without pay when poor weather made the scheduled work impossible whereas in happier times some light tasks around the farmstead would have been found. There were reports of men being out of work during the winter from many parts of the eastern counties in the early 1880s. By 1885 there were even said to be some unemployed during the summer months, but by then it was the more significant measures to achieve economies that were having effect.

One of these was the mechanisation of the corn harvest. The use of machinery was one of the principal reasons for the decline in agricultural employment cited before a committee of investigation appointed by the Board of Agriculture in 1906.[16] It was the reaper and the self-binder which had been largely responsible. The strikes of the early 1870s prompted many eastern farmers to take an interest in harvesting machines who had not seriously considered them before. At the height of the troubles in 1873 and 1874 local newspapers reported numerous instances of the harvest being gathered with the aid of well timed purchases of machinery. The vast savings of labour made the reaping machines yet more attractive. The reaper could cut nearly nine times as much corn in a day as could be done using scythes, it required about half the labour, and cut the cost of harvesting by more than half. Seven shillings an acre compared with sixteen were the costs of harvesting by machine and by hand reported by a farmer from Spalding. The self-binder, which began to find general use in the 1890s, by cutting out the work of tying sheaves required half the labour of the ordinary reaping machine. Savings of this magnitude were irresistible. By 1900 about 80 per cent of the corn harvest was being cut by machine. In 1871 the proportion had been 25 per cent. The machines were used to displace casual harvest labour or, as happened in south-west Lancashire, to enable day labourers to be employed in place of living-in farm servants.[17]

There were other implements taken into more common use. Elevators helped in the stacking of both corn and hay harvests. Mowers and hay tedders were to be found even on the smallest farms in Wales, where the cost of labour was of as much concern as on the corn farms of East Anglia. Potato diggers began to find favour during the 1890s.

Given almost equal importance to machinery in replies to the Board of Agriculture's inquiry on labour in 1906 was the effect of changes in farming practice which substituted labour-saving for labour-demanding crops. Wheat, the most labour-intensive of the cereal crops, was in decline. So, too, were roots, which required constant attention with weeding and singling. In general on tillage land there were attempts to dispense with some of the more thorough cultivations deemed essential earlier in the century. In place of wheat, and corn generally, grass was being sown, which represented an enormous saving of labour. In some districts where there was little tradition of pastoral husbandry it was the saving in cost that most prompted farmers to sow the grass.

The results of all the labour-saving exercises were a disappointment for the farmers. In his survey of Bedfordshire for the Royal Commission of 1893 Mr Hunter Pringle reported that the high cost of labour had done more to keep the costs of production up than anything else, especially on strong (clay) land arable farms. He went on to cite a number of examples of farms where the cost of labour was little changed despite such expedients as laying land down to grass. Indeed, it was not unusual for labour to take a larger part of total expenses. On one of Hunter Pringle's examples in Bedfordshire, a farm of 260 acres, labour, 8·1 per cent of the total in 1882, became 10·2 per cent in 1893. On another farm near Lincoln 20 per cent of gross expenses went on labour in 1883–84 and 25 per cent in 1893–94, and on a farm in south Dorset the rise was from 33 per cent in 1876 to 38 per cent in 1892. On the basis of evidence such as this the Royal Commission concluded that 'the farmer has not yet been able in the matter of labour to adjust his expenditure to his diminished receipts'.[18] In the later 1890s the task of adjustment became yet harder, for migration to the towns was bringing about labour shortages, with consequent increases in wages.

After rent and labour the items on the farmer's expenditure account were relatively small, and so, consequently, were the potential economies. The main categories were rates and taxes, feed and manures. The first was largely outside the farmers' control and was immensely unpopular. The 'burden on the land', the alleged unfair distribution of taxation and especially local rates between land and other forms of property, was a perennial object of dissatisfaction and a prominent issue in the agricultural politics of the time. Farmers' complaints could be supported by the fact that rates in the pound were generally rising. This should perhaps have meant that farmers were paying more in rates and taxes, and for some that was true. On the whole, however, farmers' accounts indicate that this item remained more or less constant, and sometimes fell, for some by as much as 50 per cent. This was mainly the outcome of reduced assessments to rates. Some poor-law unions carried out complete revaluations, but even in those that did not the farmers' liability was likely to be reduced by the fact that rates were assessed on rental values, which generally were falling. The same was true with taxes, and was one of the main reasons why farmers preferred their landlords to help by making full reductions of rent rather than remissions which did not count when rates and taxes were assessed. Further savings came at the end of the century when the political pressure brought about the Agricultural Rating Act, 1896, which relieved the farmer of half of his rates.

The amount spent on feed, seed and fertiliser depended on the type of agriculture practised. There were two broad options facing farmers. One was to cut the amount bought and to rely almost entirely on home-grown supplies, even if that meant reducing the total nutrition returned to the land. There were times when almost all farmers took this course. When the price of wheat was falling to its lowest, in 1893–96, feeding one's own corn to the stock and saving on the cake bill seemed the most sensible thing to do. But not all did this as a regular practice, for with livestock farming offering the prospect of return there was every incentive for farmers to take advantage of low prices of corn and cake to maintain or increase their purchases of feedingstuffs.

Ultimately, cutting the costs of farming proved to be a most difficult exercise. Labour was the main expenditure from which economies might be expected, yet all the efforts failed to make much impression on the total bill. That left the majority of farmers dependent on their landlords, who offered the greatest savings through reductions in rent which were at least in proportion to the decline in prices of the principal farm products of each district. The landlord's assistance did not stop at reducing rent. Remissions came on top of that, and in the main arable regions these came to be almost permanent fixtures, not the temporary help they were theoretically supposed to be. Farmers expected them to continue indefinitely, even after prices began to rise in the late 1890s. When Edward Heneage, one of the large landowners in north Lincolnshire, gave notice to his tenants in 1899 that he intended to discontinue the remission granted in previous years, he was met by a chorus of protest from the farmers declaring that times were still desperately hard and that 10 per cent remission would make all the difference between survival and bankruptcy.[19]

In the arable counties landlords had to accept a growing burden of rent arrears. They were mostly incurred during the worst years, 1878–81, but the weakness of arable farming was such that tenants were rarely able to pay them off. There were arrears equal to about 10 per cent of the rental on the Wilton estate throughout the 1880s. One of the Earl of Yarborough's tenants on his Brocklesby estate in the Lincolnshire wolds owed £4,547 in 1892, and the following year nearly £30,000 of accumulated arrears were written off, such was the unprofitability of corn and sheep farming. Landlords gave further help through subsidies of manure, coal and timber, and often by taking on the payment of tithe. And, although they did cut back during the 1880s and 1890s, landlords continued to spend uneconomically large sums on the repair and improvement of their estates. Lord Petre's agent remarked in 1893 that he would have been better off putting £1,000 a year on deposit than spending over £3,000 a year on the estate as he had done. In the early 1880s landlords generally had increased expenditure on their estates to counteract the effects of the depression. In particular they had spent generously on underdrainage to repair the damage of the wet seasons. But as the years dragged on with little sign of improvement

Table 4 The cost of growing wheat and barley on wold land, per acre

	Wheat			Barley		
	£	s	d	£	s	d
(a) 1879–80						
Rent and tithe	1	16	0	1	16	0
Rates and taxes		5	0		5	0
Seed		18	0		18	0
Manure	2	0	0			
Cultivation	1	5	0	2	0	0
Labour, inc. threshing and markets		10	0		10	0
Sundries		8	0			
Total	7	2	0	5	9	3
(b) 1891–94						
Rent		18	8		18	8
Seed		8	9½		10	6
Cultivation	1	4	1	1	5	2
Reaping, threshing and delivering	1	2	11	1	4	5
Weeding		1	0		1	0
Rates and taxes		3	5½		3	5½
Manure	1	5	0			
Sundries		12	0		12	0
Total	7	0	10	5	11	2½

Source. RC Agricultural Interest, Second Report of S. B. L. Druce, pp. 57–9. RC Agriculture 1893, Report of A. Wilson Fox on Lincolnshire, pp. 142–3.

the owners of arable estates had no choice but to cut back before all of their diminishing rent roll disappeared into expenditure on repairs. Those with estates in the pastoral regions were in a better position, and the Earl of Bective was apparently quite content with his expenditure of £119,000 on his estate in Cumberland over the fifteen years to 1894.[20]

It was the landlord, then, who had to carry much of the burden of arable farming's unprofitability. Just how unprofitable corn-growing was can be seen from table 4. The cost of growing wheat and barley on wold land had hardly changed between 1880 and 1893, despite reductions in rent and the widespread use of reaping machines. Making economies was not enough, and more radical changes in farming methods had to be found if farmers were to earn profits.

Notes

1. RC Agricultural Interest 1879, reports of assistant commissioners. F. M. L. Thompson, 'Agriculture since 1870', *Victoria County History, Wiltshire*, iv, 1959, p. 104.

2. RC Agricultural Interest 1879, qq. 53606–8, 62672. W. E. Bear, 'The survival in farming', *Journal of the Royal Agricultural Society of England*, lii, 1891, p. 272.

3. W. E. Bear, 'The survival in farming', *Journal of the Royal Agricultural Society of England*, lii, 1891, pp. 265–72.

4. E. P. Squarey, 'Farm capital', *Journal of the Royal Agricultural Society of England*, xxxix, 1878, p. 437. *Agricultural Gazette*, 27 December 1880.

5. F. M. L. Thompson, 'Agriculture since 1870', *Victoria County History, Wiltshire*, iv, 1959, p. 98.

6. RC Agriculture 1893, Report of Henry Rew on Salisbury Plain, p. 15, Report of A. Wilson Fox on Lincolnshire, p. 125.

7. P. J. Perry, 'Where was the "Great Agricultural Depression?" ', in P. J. Perry (ed.), *British Agriculture, 1875–1914*, 1973, pp. 129–48.

8. RC Agriculture 1893, Report of Henry Rew on Salisbury Plain, p. 14.

9. *Stamford Mercury*, 27 December 1878.

10. The example is from a letter to Henry Chaplin, 26 December 1881, Lincolnshire Archives Office, BS 13/1/13/50.

11. Joan Thirsk and Jean Imray, *Suffolk Farming in the Nineteenth Century,* 1958, pp. 99–101.

12. F. M. L. Thompson, 'Agriculture since 1870', *Victoria County History, Wiltshire,* iv, 1959, pp. 95, 104. RC Agriculture 1893, Report of A. Wilson Fox on Cumberland, pp. 25–6, Report of R. Hunter Pringle on Essex, p. 41, Report of R. Henry Rew on north Devon, p. 11. T. W. Fletcher, 'Lancashire livestock farming during the Great Depression', *Agricultural History Review,* ix, 1961, pp. 17–42. David Howell, *Land and People in Nineteenth Century Wales,* 1978, pp. 55–6.

13. F. M. L. Thompson, 'Agriculture since 1870', *Victoria County History, Wiltshire,* iv, 1959, pp. 102–4.

14. A. Wilson Fox, 'Agricultural wages in England and Wales during the last half-century', *Journal of the Royal Statistical Society,* lxvi, 1903, and reprinted in W. E. Minchinton (ed.), *Essays in Agrarian History,* 1968, ii, pp. 121–98.

15. E. L. Jones, 'The agricultural labour market in England, 1793–1872', *Economic History Review,* 2nd series, xvii, 1964–65, pp. 322–38.

16. *Report on the Decline in the Agricultural Population of Great Britain, 1881–1906* [Cd. 3273], 1906, pp. 31 ff.

17. *Agricultural Gazette,* 14 September 1885. E. J. T. Collins, *Sickle to Combine,* 1969, pp. 7, 9, 24, 28. Alistair Mutch, 'The mechanization of the harvest in south-west Lancashire, 1850–1914', *Agricultural History Review,* xxix, 1981, p. 129.

18. RC Agriculture 1893, Final Report, p. 88; Farm Accounts, p. 63, 86, 127.

19. Lincolnshire Archives Office, 2HEN 2/2/27, 72, 75.

20. F. M. L. Thompson, *English Landed Society in the Nineteenth Century,* 1963, pp. 315–16. RC Agriculture 1893, Report of A. Wilson Fox on Cumberland, p. 34. Essex Record Office, D/DPE 17. Lincolnshire Archives Office, YARB 5. F. M. L. Thompson, 'Agriculture since 1870', *Victoria County History, Wiltshire,* iv, 1959, p. 104.

3 Changing patterns 1870–1914

By the 1870s it was becoming evident that corn crops, and in particular wheat, were declining in profitability, despite the reasonably high prices then prevailing. Some farmers had been taking note and were already making adjustments to the balance within their mixed farming to make livestock more important.[1] When prices began to fall rapidly and continuously the weakness of cereals was plain for all to see, and the search for profitable alternatives became more earnest. There was no shortage of advice offered to farmers by journalists and pundits. A writer in the *Retford News* declared in 1880 that 'the farmer who has been alert to note the changes in the habits and tastes of the people, and who will adapt his produce to the requirements of his market [will] reap glorious harvests'.[2] *The Times* likewise got in quickly with the advice that 'it no longer pays to plough, and it pays to graze', and this indeed became one of the recurring themes throughout ensuing years. Farmers were assailed on all sides, from forthright leaders in the *Agricultural Gazette* to sober articles in the *Journal of the Royal Agricultural Society of England,* with the advice that they should lay some of their arable fields to pasture. Other writers offered all kinds of crops, from fruit and vegetables to sugar beet and flax, as profitable alternatives to wheat.

The assistant commissioner investigating Essex for the Royal Commission of 1893, Hunter Pringle, suggested that if in the 1870s the farmers of the county had looked ahead ten or fifteen years and started to replace corn with live-stock things would have been easier for them.[3] Farmers, of course, were blessed with no greater prescience than anyone else, and adapting their husbandry proved often to be less straightforward than the leader writers, assistant commissioners and others hoped. Certainly, there was a massive reduction in the acreage of wheat. The lowest total recorded for England and Wales, 1,384,000 acres in 1895, was only 43 per cent of the 3,240,000 acres of 1875. But, as fig. 1 shows, there was no rush to abandon wheat. The change was gradual and cumulative, the steepest fall not coming until the early 1890s, when prices reached rock bottom. And, although this was to become an age when livestock and grassland held the advantage, the addition of nearly 4 million acres to the permanent pasture of the country was the result as much of steady accumulation as of wholesale conversion following the bad years around 1879. Nearly a third of the half-million acres added in 1879

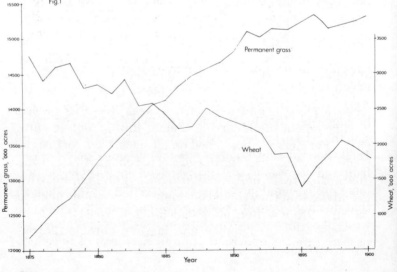

Fig. 1

34

and 1880 came as a result of leaving temporary grass down as permanent pasture.

Farmers were carrying on in the expectation that the prices of cereals would not keep on falling. They were concerned with the effects of the weather, and as far as they could see there was no need to rush into radical changes. Some land, especially heavy land, was left down in grass. After two or three wet years it was often so out of condition that there was little else to do with it. The pasture was of poor, often 'tumbledown', quality which farmers had every intention of ploughing up within a few years, although that was seldom fulfilled. Other land was given more scientific treatment as new pasture, but again the results were often dubious.[4]

There were several other reasons why farmers proceeded slowly. To some extent they were unsure how best to adapt their husbandry. Brought up in the belief that farming systems such as the sheep-and-corn husbandry of the light chalk lands were the best means of yielding results and conserving fertility, they were at a loss to see how else to farm their land. 'If the Wolds cannot be farmed as they are now they must go out of cultivation,' the Royal Commission's representative in Lincolnshire was told in the 1890s. Mixed in with these sentiments was no doubt a certain amount of plain conservatism. There was also a sort of agricultural snobbishness emanating from the prestige which had been built up around cereals. A writer in the *Agricultural Gazette* gave expression to this feeling when he suggested that to lay land down to grass was an admission that the art of farming had failed. The *Retford News* in 1880 thought that farmers should pay more attention to fruit and vegetables instead of the 'less profitable, though more professional pursuit of corn-growing'.[5] Pride such as that no doubt helped encourage farmers in such places as west Berkshire and Wiltshire to continue ploughing up pasture into the mid 1870s, and to be reluctant to reduce their dependence on corn in the 1880s.[6]

Farmers were also unsure that changing their farming radically was going to be profitable. They could see the losses on their wheat easily enough, but were dubious about the alternatives, and, having lost a lot of capital, were not in a position to make rapid changes. The same reasoning applied to landlords, who usually had to foot the bill for major works such as underdraining, buildings, and laying down land to grass. It was expensive to create good new pastures, especially on heavy clays or thin soils in the dry parts of eastern and midland England. James Howard reckoned it cost £3 10s to £4 per acre to convert arable to grass in Bedfordshire, His neighbour, the Duke of Bedford, put the cost as high as £15 an acre for some of the clays at Woburn.[7] The duke was no enthusiast for converting arable to grass. With the rent of those fields at Woburn no more than 5s an acre, his investment was hardly profitable. His was an extreme example, but not exceptional. After a wide-ranging study James Caird came to the conclusion that a large proportion of the new-laid pasture was unprofitable.[8] Farmers had similar doubts. Livestock may have been the way to profits, but prices were moving downwards, even though more slightly than those of corn, and there were plenty of cautionary tales of people caught by a low market losing all they had spent on feed, and of others embarking on livestock enterprises and coming unstuck. There was Mr Sheriff, at Hatfield in Hertfordshire, who started farming in 1892, followed the trend of the times by fattening bullocks, and lost £400 on the year. He next tried his hand at rearing calves and lost heavily again.[9] That type of experience not only dispirited those who suffered, but deterred neighbours who heard about it. Mr Sheriff in fact perserved and became a successful breeder of pedigree Shorthorns, but for most farmers the reaction was to be cautious about embarking on new enterprises. Instead, they made piecemeal changes, gradually gaining experience, and all the while hoping that lower rents would make a difference to their arable operations.

Everywhere corn-growing was in decline, with a decrease of 24 per cent in the acreage in England and Wales between 1875 and 1900. It was in the established pastoral areas where farmers showed greater eagerness to abandon corn and concentrate on their natural advantages for keeping livestock on grass. Transport was now so good that there was no great need to grow cereals for local and regional markets, and at the prices of the time there was no profit in it. What was grown was predominantly to feed cattle, but with cereal prices falling so heavily it was often more sensible to buy feed grains from arable farmers. So it was that in Northumberland arable cropping declined by about forty per cent in twenty years as the upland dales were sown to permanent grass, leaving cereal-growing concentrated along the coastal strip. In Derbyshire corn crops declined by 36 per cent in acreage between 1875 and 1900. The average decline for Wales was some 27 per cent.[10] These changes were a continuation, sometimes a hastening, of a trend which had set in several years before the onset of falling prices in the 1870s. The greater returns from livestock had already induced the farmers of Shropshire to reduce their sowings of wheat – around Oswestry, for example – by as much as 40 per cent between 1854 and 1870. The acreage of arable land in Wensleydale had been halved between the 1850s and the 1870s.[11]

Wheat bore the brunt of the decline in cereal farming in pastoral areas. With no profit as a cash crop, almost the only justification for growing it was as a source of straw for bedding. The acreage devoted to wheat was commonly reduced by half, sometimes more, between 1875 and 1900. In the North Riding the decline was 59 per cent, in Shropshire 61 per cent, and in Westmorland nearly 87 per cent, which all but made the crop unknown in that county.

Barley and oats, with more value as feed for cattle and horses, were not given up to the same extent. Indeed, not infrequently the acreage of oats actually increased, by more than 40 per cent in Cheshire and Devon, and almost doubled in Herefordshire.

Similar substitution of other cereals for wheat took place in the lowland counties. The acreage of oats, especially, increased. In East Anglia, where oats had been little grown, the acreage more than doubled between 1875 and 1900. Elsewhere increases of 30 or 40 per cent were common. Barley, on the whole, was less grown, but in a few areas its acreage did increase. These were the light-soiled districts of eastern England particularly favoured by the brewers of Burton upon Trent for producing the finest quality malting barley. On the wolds and heath of Lincolnshire, the Yorkshire wolds, in Norfolk and Suffolk, on the stonebrash soils of Oxfordshire barley was substituted for wheat, which became a crop of minor importance in many parishes of those districts. This was one of the ways by which farmers kept in business there, for barley sold to Burton could earn at least 20 per cent above the average price. It meant also that farmers were able to get by with little change to their established pattern of arable farming. The proportion of their land sown to cereals changed little as barley replaced wheat, nor was the acreage of grass much increased.[12]

Farmers in other parts of arable England found the problem of what to do with the cereal crops more difficult. They could grow more oats for the additional livestock they might be keeping, and possibly as a cash crop, especially if there was a nearby urban market for horse fodder. It is clear, however, that farmers found difficulty in breaking away from wheat, partly perhaps from traditional attachment, partly because they found it necessary as part of any arable rotation, partly because they felt stuck with it, being unsure of the value of grass in dry eastern England. There

remained also the hope that, by making the right economies, and with prices rising slightly from 1895, cereal
farming might just be made to pay. In several of the eastern
and southern counties, where wheat in the 1870s might
occupy as much as a fifth, and in fenland Cambridgeshire a
quarter, of the cultivated land, the decline in wheat-growing was well below the national average. While the acreage
of wheat in England and Wales by 1900 had fallen by 45 per
cent from what it was in 1875, in Berkshire the decline was
39 per cent, Essex 37 per cent, Huntingdonshire 34 per
cent, Suffolk 27 per cent and Cambridgeshire only 24 per
cent.

Although the acreage of wheat, still less of corn crops
generally, may have been declining slowly and relatively
slightly, farmers in the arable and mixed farming districts
were taking steps to reduce their dependence on cereals. In
the first place more use was made of grass, usually adopted
as an economy measure. Often rotation grasses were preferred, at least initially, the common practice being to leave
a sowing of clover or grass down for two or three years
instead of the customary one, so extending a four or five-
year arable rotation to six, seven or more years. It was an
expedient probably more popular than the agricultural
statistics suggest, since leaving a ley down for longer than
usual made the grass a more important part of the farming
without necessarily increasing the acreage it covered.
Temporary leys were especially favoured in areas such as
the wolds and the Chilterns, the light-soiled areas which
were generally reckoned to be unsuitable for permanent
grass. It was not uncommon, however, for the leys to be left
for so many years that by the 1890s they had become
permanent pasture.[13]

The habit of leaving temporary leys to become permanent pasture was just as common in heavy-land
districts. On his tour of the counties of Bedford, Huntingdon and Northampton in 1894 Mr Hunter Pringle found

that farmers had been sowing grass nominally temporary, but leaving it for as long as the price of corn remained low and the grass itself was in good condition.[14] That in practice made the pasture permanent. Hunter Pringle made much of another irregular method of adding to pasture, simply leaving land to seed itself. Two-thirds of the pasture on the Essex clays, he reckoned, was of this tumbledown quality. He was perhaps exaggerating. Certainly there was a considerable amount of heavy land sown intentionally as permanent grass. The Duke of Bedford alone seeded 1,308 acres on his estate in Bedfordshire and Buckinghamshire. Land was sown properly to grass in Essex, as often as not by landlords desperate to persuade someone to take on a vacant farm. However created, the new permanent pasture made a significant difference to the pattern of farming. Acreage increased by 62 per cent in Essex between 1875 and 1900, 44 per cent in Huntingdonshire, 50 per cent in Berkshire, 70 per cent in Hampshire. The average for England and Wales was 25 per cent.

Despite the magnitude of the changes, none of those counties could be classed as pastoral by 1900. Permanent grass covered only 34 per cent of the farmland of Essex in 1900, 40 per cent in Huntingdonshire. Locally things were different. In several parishes in the clay lands of south and mid Essex, in Huntingdonshire, in south Kesteven about half the land, sometimes a little more, was under permanent grass by 1900. In the midland districts where there was a tradition of grazing, three-quarters of the county of Leicester, and two-thirds of Northampton, were now sown to pasture.

One of the benefits of temporary leys, according to Joseph Darby, writing in 1896, was that light-land farmers should be enabled to keep large flocks of sheep cheaply on home-grown fodder. Hunter Pringle thought the same should apply to farming on the heavier land in Bedfordshire and Huntingdonshire. In 1876 a survey conducted by the Royal

Agricultural Society of England had shown farmers generally to favour sheep as the best animals to keep. There were two saleable products, meat and wool. Sheep required less labour and housing than cattle, and as an integral part of the mixed farming system of lowland England they could not be bettered. They ate roots and corn grown on the farm, and, fed on cake as well, produced the best manure.[15]

The hope of all those reporters for an expansion of sheep farming was not fulfilled. The sheep population of England and Wales on the eve of war in 1914 was lower by a fifth of what it had been in the early 1870s (fig. 2). It was in lowland England that sheep farming made its greatest retreat. Numbers were reduced by a quarter between 1875 and 1900 in Lincolnshire, Norfolk and Worcestershire, by 30 per cent in Wiltshire and Leicestershire, and 37 per cent in Berkshire. The further sharp fall in numbers just before the Great War took the total loss to well over half in a number of counties.[16]

The outbreaks of disease between 1879 and 1881 caused immense damage, particularly in some of these lowland counties. The number of sheep never fully recovered. In

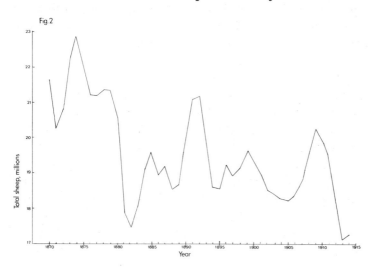

Fig. 2

part that was due to the farmers having insufficient capital to rebuild their flocks. But in addition the value of sheep to lowland farming seemed to be diminishing. The sheep's justification, especially on light lands, had mainly been that it helped build up the soil's fertility for the wheat crop. With less wheat being grown, with leys being sown as less costly than roots, with artificial fertilisers being used on the wheat crops, the sheep's place in the system of farming was diminished. Added to that was the drastic fall in the price of wool, which destroyed the sheep's claims to be producing income for the farm.

There remained the prospect of profit from mutton, and it was on that basis that some farmers in the arable–sheep districts were claiming by the turn of the century that the flock was a most profitable part of their farming. In reaching that state they had made a number of changes to their sheep husbandry. In the first place, the breeder was now most likely to fatten his own sheep. Hitherto farmers on the Cotswold hills, the Lincolnshire wolds or Norfolk had bred sheep to be sold as yearlings to graziers in the Gloucestershire vales and the fens. Two things went against the continuance of that system. Although the market for mutton was firmer, the trend of prices was downwards, and this ate away the grazier's profit margin. The second factor was the growing demand for younger, more tender meat, produced from sheep matured at one year instead of two, which rather took away the need for a specialist grazier. For the farmer on the light-soiled uplands, though, the benefits were substantial. Being his own grazier gave him flexibility in deciding when to sell; he had rapid turnover by selling fatstock younger; he was as often as not cutting his costs by having more land under grass and using less cake; and he had wool as well as meat to sell. This was why some of the light-land farmers were pleased with their flocks.[17] Their success meant that standards of breeding arable sheep were maintained.[18] It also kept the numbers of sheep up in some of the light land areas, though rarely did they match the figures of the 1870s, hence the disappointment of Joseph Darby at the results of expanding ley farming. The converse was that in the old fenland feeding districts, for example, the numbers of sheep fell by up to 50 per cent.

The demand for younger mutton caused farmers to turn from the long-woolled breeds, the Cotswold, Leicester and Lincoln, which had dominated sheep farming in midland England. These were primarily wool producers, which matured slowly into rather coarse mutton. They suffered the additional disadvantage that their long wool was out of fashion and fetching lower prices than the short staples. Breeds with short wool and which grew rapidly into tender joints became more popular. Hampshire and Oxford Downs spread into the Cotswolds, Shropshire Downs into Worcestershire. Hampshire Downs and Down crosses ceased to be curiosities at the major fairs of the Lincolnshire wolds. The Dorset Horn, valued for the fattening of lambs because they were dropped early in the year, spread east from its native county at least as far as the Vale of Aylesbury.[19]

The short-woolled sheep did not make a clean sweep. The men of Lincoln remained loyal to their breed and set about improving its mutton, introducing some Down blood to help in the process. The Lincoln was also saved by its reputation as breeding stock, especially overseas. A healthy demand grew up for rams, especially from South America, Australia and New Zealand, which resulted, in the peak of 1897, in 5,561 animals being exported, and prices reaching as high as 1,000 guineas. There were a few large-scale specialist breeders, such as Henry Dudding of Riby and R. & W. Wright of Nocton, but with the trade expanding so much there was room for the less specialised tenant farmers on the wolds and heath to take a share.[20]

William Stratton, one of the largest farmers in chalkland Wiltshire, made a more drastic change in his sheep farming when he introduced upland breeds, Cheviots and Scottish

Blackface. He used them to stock large areas of light arable land that had been allowed to fall back to poor pasture. He was able by this means to get some return from the land with the minimum of outlay. The labour bill on a farm of 732 acres, which had been £700 a year as arable, came down to £110. Stratton found imitators among his neighbours, and hill breeds became common, both here and in neighbouring Berkshire, where the Cheviot was probably the most numerous breed after the Hampshire Down. Border Leicesters and Exmoor Horns joined the ranks of upland sheep imported into this area. The extra hardiness of these breeds was exploited through what were known as 'flying flocks', sheep bought in autumn, over-wintered and sold late in spring.[21]

Sheep farming in the uplands was generally in a happier state, principally because of its low cost. Purchased feeds were modest in amount and falling in price. Rents were low, and the cost of labour was kept to a minimum by the small farmers who relied on their own families.[22] There had also been far less loss from disease at the end of the 1870s, so that farmers were not struggling to rebuild their flocks. Instead they were better able to take advantage of the healthy demand for meat and expand their business. The sheep population in a number of hill counties increased markedly between 1875 and 1900, by a fifth in Durham and Montgomery, for instance, and as much as a third in Cardiganshire.

Similar advantages were enjoyed by cattle farmers in the upland zone. They too had expanding markets for meat and milk to supply. Their costs were kept down by the use of family labour and by the cheapness of feedingstuffs, including grain, which could be bought from farmers in the lowlands. Despite the low prices and difficult seasons of the early 1890s, Wilson Fox found that the farmers of Lancashire and Cumberland had come through quite well, with little sign of depression, although the farming families had had to work hard with little reward to achieve that.[23]

The numbers of cattle kept in England and Wales increased by 15 per cent from 4,870,000 in 1875 to 5,607,000 in 1900. Continuation of the trend took the increase to 17 per cent by 1913. The pastoral counties shared in this movement. In Cumberland the increase was above the national average, as it was also in Northumberland. But some of the greatest changes were in the arable counties. Norfolk recorded an increase of 23 per cent between 1875 and 1900, Lincolnshire 25 per cent, Berkshire 27 per cent, Wiltshire 30 per cent and Hampshire 39 per cent. Many of the additional animals were bought to stock the expanded acreage of permanent pasture, but farmers were also keeping more cattle in conjunction with their arable. Farmers around Chelmsford, for example, hardly changed the basic management of their land. The predominantly arable mixed farming remained, but corn was now fed to bullocks, which had become the main source of income.[24] The effects of such changes can be seen in farm accounts. Revenue from cattle increased by 91 per cent in nine years from 1885–86 to 1893–94 on a farm near Lincoln. A fenland farmer who earned 9 per cent of his income from cattle when he started farming in 1887 was deriving 21 per cent from that source by 1900.[25]

Cattle farming followed sheep in fattening stock for sale at an earlier age. It was an idea which had been pioneered by a few farmers in southern England during the 1850s. The depression brought more farmers to take up the practice, such that selling bullocks at from sixteen to twenty months became quite commonplace. 'One great advantage,' commented William Ellis of Shalford, near Guildford, 'appears to be that whether the bullocks are twelve months old or sixteen months, they are always "beef". We can therefore suit ourselves as to when they go to market. If trade is bad, we slacken, and sometimes hold over for two months, and, then, with markets better, out they go.'[26] The

45

flexibility was added to when farmers bred their own stock to feed. Early fattening meant that capital was being turned over more quickly, while the produce was beef of high quality, and therefore more rewarding in price. The system also suited the arable farmers, who were able to use home-grown or purchased feed as they saw fit.

A greater change in cattle farming was the expansion of dairying. The number of cows returned in the June census as in calf or in milk increased by 18·6 per cent between 1871–75 and 1896–1900, and by 1911–15 the increase was 31·6 per cent, well above the 25 per cent growth in total cattle numbers. Dairying's expansion followed the sharp shocks experienced in 1878–80, when the market was glutted with cheese imported from America. Best-quality Cheshire cheese, 84s a hundredweight in 1874, was 74s in 1878–79. Lower grades fell from 50s to 25s a hundredweight. Other types of cheese fell by similar proportions, to prices that rendered it virtually unsaleable, and butter was no more profitable. Richard Jefferies summed up the common plight when he portrayed a Wiltshire dairy farmer looking over his accounts, which told 'a story somewhat at variance with the prevalent belief that dairy farming is the only branch of farming that is still profitable'.[27]

It was a severe slump, but short-lived. When Mr Coleman came to investigate dairy farming in Cheshire for the Duke of Richmond's commission in 1881 he found recovery was under way. Competition in the cheese market was receding after the price had been forced so low as to make the imports unprofitable. Meanwhile English farmers had been finding effective ways of meeting competition. The quality of cheese and butter was improved to meet the criticism that imported goods could be guaranteed to be a set standard from batch to batch whereas the home produce was extremely variable. Especially important in this respect were the factories able to standardise the manufacture of cheese in large quantities. They concentrated on a few types only, however, with the result that Cheddar, Cheshire and Stilton came to dominate the market while some of the local varieties of Wiltshire and the midland counties disappeared. The first factories opened in Derbyshire in the early 1870s, and their demand for milk in quantity boosted the growth of dairying in that county. Factory processing spread during the years to 1914. The first Wensleydale cheese factory opened at Hawes in 1897, to be followed by five more in the district during the next few years. A factory in Wiltshire to make soft cheese opened in 1888, and a butter factory at Devizes in 1910. The Anglo-Swiss Condensed Milk Company had set up business in an old cloth mill at Chippenham in 1873, and shortly afterwards had factories at Aylesbury and Middlewich as well.

At the end of the 1880s some of the cheese factories in Derbyshire were closing. They had become victim almost of their own success, for the farmers, after discovering the benefits of selling milk rather than making their own cheese, began to find more profitable outlets in the markets for liquid milk. Already in 1880 5½ million gallons of milk were carried by the Midland Railway from Derbyshire to London, with some village stations handling 6,000 gallons each week. By 1888 the traffic had increased to 8,393,292 gallons.[28] This trade came to dominate dairy farming, not only in that county but in all the main dairying districts. London was by far the largest market. By 1900 about 53 million gallons of milk were brought to the capital by rail, compared with 40 million gallons in 1890 and 9 million in 1870. Supplies were drawn from places as far as 200 miles away in Cheshire, parts of Wales and Devon, although most came from the Great Western Railway's territory from Berkshire to Somerset, and from Staffordshire and Derbyshire in the Midlands.[29] Other urban areas provided local and regional markets, the Lancashire towns for

47

farmers in Cheshire, Lancashire and Cumberland, the West Riding towns for dairymen in the Yorkshire dales.

The milk trade seemed to have everything in its favour. It was the one item of farm produce guaranteed to be free from foreign competition. Demand from major urban markets was growing, while the old-established town cowkeepers had almost all been swept away following the cattle plague of 1865. With railways extending more deeply into the countryside, and with churns and milk vans which could deliver the milk in good condition, farmers were well placed to supply the markets efficiently and profitably.

Of course, there were arguments against the milk business. It required stricter management of the herd to maintain regular calving and a supply of milk day in and day out. Feed was likely to be expensive, especially in winter. Some landlords were anxious that it might impoverish the land, since the skimmed milk fed to pigs was not being returned, as happened with farmhouse cheese-making. The organisation and cost of churns and transport to the railway station could prove irksome. All such considerations, though, were generally outweighed by the prospect of regular income and firm prices. In early 1879 wholesale prices for milk were of the order of 8*d*–9*d* a gallon of seventeen pints in summer, and up to 1*s* 8*d* a gallon in winter. Cheese at 50*s* a hundredweight was reckoned equivalent to liquid milk at just under 5*d* a gallon.[30] Small wonder, then, that almost all dairy farmers within two or three miles of a railway station took to selling milk.

Farmers in the established dairying counties were first to benefit. Cheshire remained the county where dairying was most concentrated. A density of 183·9 cows per thousand acres in 1875 had become 200·3 by 1900. Lancashire was not far behind, with 167·3 cows per thousand acres in 1900, and Derbyshire, Staffordshire, Somerset and Dorset retained their place as leading dairy counties. But dairying also expanded rapidly in other areas where hitherto it had been of modest proportions or rarely practised at all. The number of dairy cows in Cumberland increased by 24·6 per cent between 1875 and 1900 as farmers gained access to the north-western towns. In Wiltshire dairying, already established in the northern clay vale, spread into the vale of Pewsey, an arable district until the 1870s. One farmer, Frank Stratton, built up a business covering 25,000 acres with 2,000 cows by taking over vacant arable farms and laying them down to grass. Dairy farming also grew rapidly in Berkshire, where the number of cows increased by 34·7 per cent between 1875 and 1900, and in the Chiltern vales of Hertfordshire.[31]

The place where dairying attracted most notice was Essex. It was not an entirely new type of farming to the county. It was the Eastern Counties Railway that pioneered the transport of country milk to London in the 1840s. However, dairying was almost entirely neglected in Essex until the 1870s and the collapse of cereal farming on the heavy clay soils. It was then that farmers used to dairying in Scotland and the West Country began to move into the county, attracted by the extremely low rents. They set about adapting Essex agriculture to dairy farming to supply the London milk market, and brought with them not only their experience but their own cows, so that the Ayrshire became one of the common breeds of the county. Land was converted to permanent pasture, but an important part of the dairy farming here was the use of the fertile soils to feed the cows with home-grown cereals, roots and green fodder crops. Essex's native farmers began to follow this lead. Among them was the Hon. Edward Strutt, who undertook the management of the home farms on the estate of his brother, Lord Rayleigh. Several farms were given up by the tenants during the bad seasons of 1878 to 1881. Finding them difficult to let, Strutt decided to keep them in hand and introduce intensive arable dairying. He kept more of the land arable than most of his neighbours, offsetting the higher cost by concentrating on autumn calving to catch the higher-priced winter market. By 1914 Strutt's farms covered 6,000 acres.[32] Dairy farming in Essex recorded a most remarkable rate of growth. The number of cows increased by 55 per cent between 1875 and 1900. That still left the county's dairying minute in comparison with that of Cheshire, but in the heavy clayland parishes the management and fortunes of the farming had been transformed.

For farmers in certain areas of the country the smaller branches of agriculture offered the chance of profit. One of these was potato-growing in the fenlands of Lincolnshire. The acreage of potatoes in the county increased by 58 per cent between 1875 and 1900, more than three times the increase recorded for England and Wales as a whole. Almost all that gain was in the fens, where by 1900 the crop was of major importance, in some parishes taking up almost a quarter of the agricultural land. It was a risky crop. The costs of cultivation were high, about £15 an acre being the common reckoning. Disease could destroy a crop, and in years of glut prices would plummet. But in other years farmers stood to make a fortune, or at the very least a comfortable living. It was this crop that formed the basis of the prosperity to be found in the fens when Rider Haggard visited the area in 1900–01. Small farmers were able to earn a living from potatoes, but the bulk of the trade passed into the hands of large farmers who held vast acreages on which they alternated wheat and potatoes. Probably the largest of these enterprises was that of William Dennis, who had 4,000 acres, 1,500 of them growing potatoes.[33]

The fenland farmers were among the most fortunate in England, for their soil was so rich that almost anything could be grown, and this was exploited to produce the vegetable and fruit crops from which returns were particularly high. Cabbages, cauliflower and celery were among the vegetables grown as field crops, often in rotation with potatoes. Mustard was grown, mainly in Norfolk, under contract to Colman's. The growing of bulbs and flowers was developing into a sizeable business around Spalding during the 1890s. And fruit was grown, principally in Cambridgeshire, where there was a local concentration of some 4,000 acres under soft fruit around Wisbech.[34]

Nationally, the cultivation of fruit was expanding rapidly, encouraged by strong demand both for fresh fruit and from the makers of jam. The acreage under orchard in England and Wales increased by 50 per cent between 1875 and 1900. Small fruit was not recorded in the annual census until the 1890s. In 1891–95 there were 61,000 acres, which by 1911–15 had grown to 76,000 acres. An estimate for 1881 suggested there had then been about 37,000 acres of small fruit. The change was least in the established fruit-growing regions of the West Country. The principal crop there was apples for cider, but scope for development was limited. Instead growers began to turn to dessert apples, pears, plums and bush fruit to meet the growing market for fresh fruit. In Worcestershire this movement led to an increase of 50 per cent in the acreage between 1875 and 1900.[35] Outside the cider country, Kent joined the leading half-dozen counties for orchard fruit after more than doubling the acreage, to reach 26,000 acres by 1900. Kent was also by far the most important county for small fruit, having more than 22,000 acres. Elsewhere, county totals, both for orchard and for small fruit, were small, but had increased rapidly, often two or three times over in twenty-five years. There were some concentrations of local importance, such as the strawberry beds around Swanwick in Hampshire, and the fruit grown for the jam factory at Tiptree in Essex.

The acreage devoted to market-garden crops increased nearly threefold between the 1870s and 1890s. A large part of this development was in areas distant from the urban markets as railway transport allowed other advantages of local soil or climate to be exploited. There were thus large increases in acreage in Cornwall, Worcestershire, the fens of Norfolk, Cambridge and Lincolnshire, and in Bedfordshire. The importance of good transport for taking the produce away and for bringing manure back from the towns was particularly apparent in Bedfordshire, where the market gardening was concentrated in some half-dozen parishes crossed by the line of the Great Northern Railway. Here, in the district around Sandy and Potton, market gardeners and larger farmers were growing brussels sprouts, potatoes, onions and carrots for the London market. Farther south, in the Chilterns, farmers who were within two or three miles of a station took up growing vegetables, mainly potatoes.[36]

The British agricultural industry was considerably smaller in 1900 than it had been in 1870. Estimates of gross output suggest a fall of 16·7 per cent in agricultural production in the United Kingdom, and a slightly smaller decline, of 13·5 per cent, from England (table 5). Increases in some livestock products, particularly milk, were not enough to counteract the enormous decline in the value of cereals. On the eve of war in 1914 home agriculture was supplying only 42 per cent of the food consumed in the United Kingdom.[37]

Contemporary commentators found the performance of agriculture disappointing. They would point to the imports of butter worth £16 million a year, to the imports of fruit and vegetables, and suggest that there were opportunities being missed of capturing expanding and profitable markets. There was disappointment, too, at the slow progress of livestock farming, with the numbers of animals not rising in step with the extension of permanent pasture. In the whole of Great Britain, declared W. J. Malden, there were 222,000 more cattle in 1894 than 1874, whereas on the basis of the increased acreage of grassland that figure should have been nearer a million.[38] It was clear, therefore,

Table 5 Gross output of agriculture in the United Kingdom and England (£ million)

	United Kingdom		England	
	1870–76	1894–1903	1867–71	1894–98
Wheat	27·56	7·72	28·44	7·64
Barley	17·56	9·43	12·62	7·54
Oats	9·07	8·07	4·28	4·23
Potatoes	13·82	11·34	3·00	3·00
Hay, straw, fruit, vegetables	19·40	21·75	14·00	17·00
Other crops	7·58	3·64	3·09	2·06
Arable	94·99	61·95	65·43	41·47
Beef	45·67	42·05	14·59	16·02
Mutton	30·51	25·20	14·60	12·59
Pigmeat	22·95	19·13	9·59	10·52
Horses	2·00	3·00	1·00	2·00
Milk	38·51	43·56	15·40	20·29
Wool	8·27	3·24	5·62	2·36
Poultry and eggs	6·96	10·00	3·50	7·00
Livestock	154·87	146·18	64·30	70·78
Total	249·86	208·13	129·73	112·25

Source. T. W. Fletcher, 'The Great Depression of English agriculture, 1873–96', *Economic History Review*, second series, xiii, 1961, reprinted in W. E. Minchinton (ed.), *Essays in Agrarian History,* 1968, ii, p. 256.

that farmers were not investing in the new types of farming that might bring them profit. They were not increasing the yield from their crops. They were cutting back on labour and on purchases of cake and fertiliser and ignoring new techniques such as silage which could increase output. In short, high farming was in retreat.

There was much to be said for that argument. There were the extensive sheep runs on the Wiltshire downs. There were farms on the Essex clays that were barely cultivated. Part of the explanation perhaps for the slow progress lies in the difficulties of making a change. Tenancy agreements which restricted farmers to a prescribed rotation that would not impoverish the soil were one factor often cited. By the 1890s, though, that problem had been all but overcome, and most landlords allowed their tenants a free hand to choose what crops to sow. The bigger problem was the debilitating loss of capital in the late 1870s. Farmers could not afford to restock their land. There was a shortage of buildings suitable for livestock in areas where arable predominated, and one of the things that made tenants impatient with their landlords was having to persuade them to build or repair cowsheds. The contrast with those regions where livestock was already important in the 1870s was marked, and was brought out in all the reports of Royal Commissions and others. For even the smallest hill farmer was cushioned against the worst effects of falling prices and needed to do little to adapt to the changing circumstances. In the lowlands farmers had to do a great deal to catch up, and found it a struggle.

In another sense commentators such as W. J. Malden or W. E. Bear were misconstruing the changes in agriculture. For another of the recurring themes was the insistence of farmers that it was high farming that would bring them a return to profitability. 'All farm highly here as the only hope of salvation,' was how one farmer at Spalding put it, and certainly there was no stinting on manures and labour with the potato, fruit and bulb crops of his district. The Lancashire dairymen said the same. Mr Rowe, at Catterall, had a farm of eighty-five acres on which he kept twenty-five cows to milk for the market in Preston. He was spending in the 1890s £250 a year on feed, nearly half his total expenditure, and as much as rent and labour combined.[39] After declining in the early 1880s the consumption of feeds and artificial fertilisers was rising again by 1890. The total consumption of fertilisers in the United Kingdom, at 1,281,000 tons for 1911–13, was almost twice the 647,000 tons of 1886–93. Of new types of fertiliser basic slag attracted most attention as beneficial to grassland. About 4,500 tons were used in 1887, whereas by 1912 imports alone amounted to 50,000 tons. Imports of feedstuffs, too, were increasing, being about 39 per cent greater in 1911–13 than they had been in 1886–93.[40] It was evident that high farming was not yet dead.

However, high farming was coming to mean something different. In the middle years of the century the emphasis had been on high consumption of feed, fertiliser and equipment to produce returns in volume. Now farmers were looking for value for money. The farmers in Spalding and dairymen in Lancashire could justify their cake and manure bills by the high value of the produce. On some of the heavy clays and light lands things were different. Returns hardly justified the expenditure, hence the sheep runs and the arable farms that were only ticking over. In the upland pastoral areas there were some notable steps in intensification of the farming, as the favourable markets for livestock made expenditure pay. Fertilisers were applied to grassland. Mowers, horse rakes, tedders and elevators were being bought by even the small farmers to make the hay harvest more efficient. Improvements were made in breeds of sheep and cattle that were kept, with, in Cumberland, for instance, greater specialisation in the management of stock. It still left hill farming backward by comparison with most of the lowlands, and the farmer's life a hand-to-mouth existence, but the change was marked.[41]

The emphasis of farming was coming to be placed not on achieving high returns from the acre of land, but on increasing the return from labour and from capital. It was the basis of Frank Stratton's dairy farming in Wiltshire, which was extensive in its use of land but was containing the employment of labour and the need for working capital. The same philosophy prevailed among the Scotsmen who were dairying in Essex. The same principles were adopted in an entirely different direction by J. Prout in Hertfordshire and George Baylis in Berkshire, who introduced the practice of continuous corn-growing, using artificial fertilisers. With land cheap, and by keeping the cost of labour to a minimum through the use of steam ploughs and harvesting machinery, they were able to make cereals pay even at 30s a quarter for wheat. Baylis built up a large enterprise, amounting to 12,140 acres by 1917, mostly on the light soils of the Berkshire downs. His methods again used land extensively, with fallows and clover grown to rest the land. Few followed his example to the letter, but the search for better returns on capital and labour was more general, and by 1900 it was paying off. For when Rider Haggard and Sir Daniel Hall made their tours of agricultural England, among the neglect and poor farming they found evidence of a new stability and a modest profitability, estimated recently at perhaps 6 per cent on capital.[42]

Notes

1. E. L. Jones, *The Development of English Agriculture, 1815–1873*, 1968, pp. 17–25. E. L. Jones, 'The changing basis of agricultural prosperity, 1852–73', *Agricultural History Review*, x, 1962, pp. 102–19.

2. *Retford News*, 26 June 1880.

3. RC Agriculture 1893, Report of R. Hunter Pringle on Essex, p. 132.

4. RC Agriculture 1893, Minutes of Evidence, q. 40903. James Caird, 'Recent experiences in laying down land to grass', *Journal of the Royal Agricultural Society of England*, xlix, 1888, p. 154.

5. *Agricultural Gazette*, 24 April 1882. *Retford News*, 26 June 1880.

6. A. G. Bradley, *When Squires and Farmers Thrived*, 1927, p.

193. F. M. L. Thompson, 'Agriculture since 1870', *Victoria County History, Wiltshire,* iv, 1959, p. 97.

7. James Howard, 'Laying down land to grass', *Journal of the Royal Agricultural Society of England,* xli, 1880, p. 436. Duke of Bedford, *A Great Agricultural Estate,* 1897, pp. 196–8.

8. James Caird, 'Recent experiences in laying down land to grass', *Journal of the Royal Agricultural Society of England,* xlix, 1888, pp. 153–4.

9. G. M. Brown, *Farming Yesterday and Today,* 1962, pp. 34, 40.

10. Statistics quoted in this chapter, unless otherwise noted, are taken from the Agricultural Returns for which national and county totals were published annually, while figures for individual parishes are kept in manuscript at the Public Record Office, class MAF68.

11. J. Philip Dodd, 'High farming in Shropshire, 1845–1870', *Midland History,* viii, 1983, p. 165. R. T. Fieldhouse, 'Agriculture in Wensleydale from 1600 to the present day', *Northern History,* xvi, 1980, p. 180.

12. John Orr, *Agriculture in Oxfordshire,* 1916, pp. 198–200.

13. J. T. Coppock, 'Agricultural changes in the Chilterns, 1875–1900', in P. J. Perry (ed.), *British Agriculture, 1875–1914,* 1973, p. 65.

14. RC Agriculture 1893, Report of R. Hunter Pringle on Bedford, Huntingdon and Northampton, p. 41.

15. Joseph Darby, 'The pastoral outlook', *Journal of the Royal Agricultural Society of England,* lvii, 1896, p. 167. RC Agriculture 1893, Report of R. Hunter Pringle on Bedford, Huntingdon and Northampton, p. 42. W. Macdonald, 'On the relative profits to the farmer from horse, cattle and sheep breeding, rearing and feeding in the United Kingdom', *Journal of the Royal Agricultural Society of England,* xxxvii, 1876, p. 1–108.

16. John Orr, *Agriculture in Oxfordshire,* 1916, p. 19. John Orr, *Agriculture in Berkshire,* 1918, p. 203. R. C. Gaut, *A History of Worcestershire Agriculture,* 1939, p. 395. Joan Thirsk, 'Agrarian history, 1540–1950', *Victoria County History, Leicestershire,* ii, 1954, p. 248. RC Agriculture 1893, Report of A. Wilson Fox on Norfolk, p. 31.

17. RC Agriculture 1893, Report of A. Wilson Fox on Lincolnshire, p. 137. *The Tariff Commission. Report of the Agricultural Committee,* 1906, para. 863.

18. RC Agriculture 1893, Report of R. Henry Rew on the Salisbury Plain district of Wiltshire, p. 18.

19. P. Anderson Graham, *The Revival of English Agriculture,* 1899, p. 84. R. C. Gaut, *A History of Worcestershire Agriculture,* 1939, p. 395. RC Agriculture 1893, Report of R. Henry Rew on Dorset, p. 7.

20.   P. Anderson Graham, *The Revival of English Agriculture,* 1899, p. 84. W. T. Carrington, 'Pastoral husbandry', *Journal of the Royal Agricultural Society of England,* xxxix, 1878, p. 711. G. E. Collins, 'Agriculture', *Victoria County History, Lincolnshire,* ii, 1906, pp. 413–14. J. W. Turner, 'The position of the wool trade', *Journal of the Royal Agricultural Society of England,* lvii, 1896, p. 72. C. E. Howard, 'Lincoln Longwools', *Lincolnshire Magazine,* ii, 1934, p. 319.

21.   RC Agriculture 1893, Report of R. Henry Rew on the Salisbury Plain district of Wiltshire, pp. 15–16. John Orr, *Agriculture in Berkshire,* 1918, p. 202.

22.   RC Agriculture 1893, Report of A. Wilson Fox on Cumberland, p. 31. Report of R. Hunter Pringle on South Durham and the North and East Ridings of Yorkshire, p. 6.

23.   RC Agriculture 1893, Report of A. Wilson Fox on the Garstang district of Lancashire, pp. 7, 14; Report of A. Wilson Fox on Cumberland, pp. 29–32. T. W. Fletcher, 'Lancashire livestock farming during the Great Depression', in P. J. Perry (ed.), *British Agriculture, 1875–1914,* 1973, pp. 77–108.

24.   RC Agriculture 1893, Minutes of Evidence, qq. 64166–80.

25.   RC Agriculture 1893, Farm Accounts, p. 128. Lincolnshire Archives Office HD65/64.

26.   Henry Evershed, 'Early fattening of cattle, especially in the counties of Sussex and Surrey', *Journal of the Royal Agricultural Society of England,* xxix, 1878, pp. 152–68. Henry Evershed, 'The early fattening of cattle and sheep', *Journal of the Royal Agricultural Society of England,* li, 1890, p. 60.

27.   *Bell's Weekly Messenger,* 13 January, 3 March 1879. Richard Jefferies, *Hodge and his Masters,* 1880.

28.   J. R. Bond, 'Derbyshire farming past and present', *Journal of the Royal Agricultural Society of England,* xciii, 1932, p. 172.

29.   P. J. Atkins, 'The growth of London's railway milk trade *c.* 1845–1914', *Journal of Transport History,* new series, iv, 1977–78, pp. 204, 216–17.

30.   RC Agricultural Interest 1879, Report of Mr Coleman on Cheshire, p. 56. *Bell's Weekly Messenger,* 3 March, 12 May 1879.

31.   F. M. L. Thompson, 'Agriculture since 1870', *Victoria County History, Wiltshire,* iv, 1959, p. 107. David Taylor, 'Some aspects of the development of English dairying, 1860–1930, and their relation to the south-west', in W. E. Minchinton (ed.), *Farming and Transport in the South West,* 1972, pp. 39–40. J. T. Coppock, 'Agricultural changes in the Chilterns, 1875–1900', in P. J. Perry (ed.), *British Agriculture, 1875–1914,* 1973, pp. 70–1.

32.   Primrose McConnell, 'Experiences of a Scotsman on the Essex clays', *Journal of the Royal Agricultural Society of England,*

lii, 1891, pp. 311–25. Sir William Gavin, *Ninety Years of Family Farming*, 1967, pp. 81–115.

33. H. Rider Haggard, *Rural England*, 1902, ii, pp. 203–7. E. A. Pratt, *The Transition in Agriculture*, 1906, p. 208.

34. E. A. Pratt, *The Transition in Agriculture*, 1906, pp. 43–7, 74–6, 81–2. E. C. Eagle, 'Some light on the beginnings of the Lincolnshire bulb industry', *Lincolnshire Historian*, No. 6 (autumn 1950), pp. 220–9.

35. R. C. Gaut, *A History of Worcestershire Agriculture*, 1939, pp. 418–31.

36. R. J. Battersby, 'The Development of Market Gardening in England, 1850–1914' (unpublished PhD thesis, University of London, 1960), pp. 33–60. F. Beavington, 'The development of market gardening in Bedfordshire, 1799–1939', *Agricultural History Review*, xxiii, 1975, pp. 31–43. J. T. Coppock, 'Agricultural changes in the Chilterns, 1875–1900', in P. J. Perry (ed.), *British Agriculture, 1875–1914*, 1973.

37. Royal Society, *The Food supply of the United Kingdom*, Cd. 8421, 1916, appendix 1a.

38. W. J. Malden, 'Recent changes in farm practices', *Journal of the Royal Agricultural Society of England*, lvii, 1896, pp. 32–3.

39. RC Agriculture 1893, Report of A. Wilson Fox on Lincolnshire, p. 40; Report of A. Wilson Fox on the Garstang district of Lancashire, pp. 14, 34.

40. E. M. Ojala, *Agriculture and Economic Progress*, 1952. F. M. L. Thompson, 'The second agricultural revolution, 1815–1880', *Economic History Review*, second series, xxi, 1968, pp. 74–7. P. J. Perry, *British Farming in the Great Depression, 1870–1914*, 1974, pp. 112–13.

41. David Howell, *Land and People in Nineteenth Century Wales*, 1978, p. 18. E. J. T. Collins, *The Economy of Upland Britain: an illustrated review*, 1978, pp. 23–4. J. D. Marshall and John K. Walton, *The Lake Counties from 1830 to the mid-twentieth Century*, 1981, pp. 62–3. RC Agriculture 1893, Report of A. Wilson Fox on Cumberland, p. 36.

42. F. M. L. Thompson, 'Agriculture since 1870', *Victoria County History, Wiltshire*, iv, 1959, pp. 107–8. C. S. Orwin, *Progress in English Farming Systems, iii, A Specialist in Arable Farming*, 1930. John Orr, *Agriculture in Berkshire*, 1918, pp. 33–4. H. Rider Haggard, *Rural England*, 1902. A. D. Hall, *A Pilgrimage of British Farming*, 1913. Peter E. Dewey, 'British farming profits and government policy during the first world war', *Economic History Review*, second series, xxxvii, 1984, p. 378.

4 Farming and food production during the First World War

Wartime brought new demands and a renewed importance to agriculture. Demand for food was strengthened. The population, 36 million in 1911, was large and growing throughout these years of war. On top of that, a fighting population required greater energy than normal. The Royal Society, in an investigation carried out for the government, reckoned that the military diet represented 4,300 calories per day, whereas the needs of an average man in peacetime civilian life were about 3,400 calories each day.[1] When the prospects were that international trade was going to be disrupted the main beneficiaries from wartime demand were likely to be British farmers.

Cereal growers stood to gain most from wartime conditions, since maintaining the supply of bread grains was bound to come first in any national strategy. Reflecting this, and the expectation that foreign competition would be reduced, prices of corn started to rise as soon as war broke out, despite the good harvest that was just being garnered. From the 34s 2d a quarter at which they stood at the beginning of August 1914, English wheat prices rose to 42s 2d in December, and by the beginning of May 1915 had reached 55s 11d. The gazette average for 1915 was 52s 10d a quarter, 51·3 per cent above the 34s 11d of 1914. Barley and oats also appreciated in anticipation of increased

60

demand for feeding people and livestock. It was not long
before the military authorities were requistioning horses
and the hay and oats to feed them. The average price of oats
was 44·2 per cent higher in 1915 than it had been in 1914,
and of barley 37·4 per cent. These changes set the tone for
the whole of the war, for, as can be seen from table 6, while
the prices of all the principal types of farm produce rose
substantially, cereals led the way until the final few
months.

Table 6 Price indices (1913–14 = 100) for farm produce
from 1914–15 to 1918–19

| | Year beginning 1 June | | | | |
	1914–15	*1915–16*	*1916–17*	*1917–18*	*1918–19*
Cereals	130	168	217	234	234
Pulse	130	155	209	369	441
Livestock	105	128	158	193	196
Dairy produce	103	132	166	197	258
Hay and straw	102	149	188	195	252
Potatoes	113	142	305	207	247

Source. RC Agriculture 1919, Minutes of Evidence, i,
appendix, p. 5.

These prices were the basis upon which farmers were
able to earn profits well above those of the immediate
pre-war years, and a complete contrast to the losses of the
1880s and 1890s. Net farm income in Great Britain rose
nearly fourfold between 1914 and 1918, from £58 million to
£173 million. Estimating the costs of family labour on the
farm to produce a truer figure for profits is difficult, but,
however calculated, the rise is substantial. The number of
farmers and their families recorded in the census of
production for 1908 differs from the total entered in the

population census of 1911. On the basis of the census of production Dr Dewey's calculations show profits of 2 per cent on capital in 1914 reached a peak of 10·6 per cent in 1917. Using the population census as the starting point proves more generous to the farmer, showing a rise from 7·5 per cent in 1914 to 14·3 per cent in 1917. Profits before the war were small by comparison, just 0·3 per cent on the low estimate, 6·1 per cent on the higher.[2]

What made the farmers' fortunes in these years was the fact that costs rose by considerably less than prices. Rent was the item most out of step, for there was barely any change at all.[3] The strongest reason, it seems, was that landowners were reluctant to increase rents at a time of national need, with the result that the few changes that were made came at changes of tenancy. The cost of labour in 1918 was two-thirds greater than it had been in 1914, though most of the increase came in the last year of war, when the government was setting minimum rates of wages. Total spending on feeds and fertiliser both rose substantially, the amounts in 1917 being 75 and 52 per cent greater than the pre-war average.

Those figures for the costs of feeds and fertiliser are in one sense misleading. The prices of many of the farmer's purchases rose enormously. Linseed cake in the year beginning June 1913 was priced at 151s 9d a ton; five years later it was two and half times more expensive, at 380s a ton. Prices of milling by-products, bran and middlings, rose by similar amounts.[4] Farmers' costs in fact were kept down as much by the impossibility of maintaining their normal employment of manures, feeds and labour as by changes in price. Supplies of all three were restricted by the disruption of overseas trade and by competition from other pressing needs in managing the nation's war effort.

Shortages of feedstuffs were severe and became progressively worse through the war years. Consumption of oilcake, supplies of which were all imported either ready-made or as raw materials, was already more than 10 per cent down in 1915 compared with the previous year. In 1918 consumption was as little as 42 per cent of what it had been in 1914. Imports of maize were similarly curtailed, so that consumption by 1918 was down to less than a third of the 1914 figure. Supplies of home-produced feeds were hardly any better, especially of cereals. The poor harvest of 1916 deprived the livestock farmer of a large part of his normal supply of feed grains. Added to that were the efforts of the Ministry of Food in taking cereals away from animals to feed to people. Barley was added to the bread flour, so that by 1917 hardly any was used for livestock feed, whereas in normal years about twenty per cent of each year's crop was used in this way. Even more successful, at least as far as feeding humans was concerned, was the policy of taking a greater proportion of milled wheat into the flour. The white flour normally milled in the pre-war years was produced from about 70 per cent of the wheat berry, leaving the remainder, the outer parts of the grain, to be used as animal feed. In order to feed more people from the wheat crop the government in November 1916 ordered this extraction rate to be raised to 76 per cent. It was subsequently raised again on several occasions, until for a time in the spring of 1918 the extraction was as high as 92 per cent. The result for livestock farmers was that consumption of wheat offals in 1918 was only 45 per cent of the pre-war average.[5] This put greater dependence on the crops of hay and roots, which, except for 1916, were no better than average.

Shortages of fertiliser were not as severe, although the difficulty of maintaining imports and the demands for munitions work upon supplies of some chemicals did have their effect. The first problem to be felt was the shortage of nitrogen as the supplies of sodium nitrate from Chile were quickly reduced. Imports in 1915 were half the previous year's and during 1916 they were cut off altogether. In

October 1915, when it seemed agriculture was going to become dangerously short of nitrogen, the Board of Agriculture set up a committee on fertilisers with the task of encouraging farmers to use ammonium sulphate, which up till then had never gained widespread use. The committee promoted its message through the press and farming organisations, and arranged with manufacturers for low prices during the spring of 1916. It gained little immediate reward for these efforts, for it was not until the corn production campaign got under way that farmers were persuaded to use ammonium sulphate, with the result that consumption in United Kingdom agriculture rose approximately threefold between 1916 and 1918. Supplies of phosphates were also reduced by 1917 as the unavailability of shipping and sinkings had cut down imports of phosphatic rocks. Consumption of superphosphates in 1917 was 31 per cent less to make good the deficiency in imports, with the result that consumption was restored.[6]

Farming lost labour to the forces, making it, according to many estimates, under strength by as much as one third. Reassessment of the evidence collected by the Board of Trade's surveys into the problem and of the amount of family labour employed on farms has moderated the estimates of labour deficiency. By 1917 farming was about 12 per cent short of its normal labour requirement, and this proportion rose to about 21 per cent as the food production campaign increased the demand for labour.[7] One of the remarkable achievements of the war was that about half of that deficiency was made up by the employment of various types of irregular labour. These were people often unused to the countryside, let alone farming, people who were unskilled, untrained and perhaps less strong than the regular farm labourers. But they were a good deal better than nothing. Indeed, in their comments made to government inquiries and in later published reminiscences farmers were generally fulsome in their praise of their

wartime helpers. As time went on and the organisation of
the irregular labour force improved so the difficulties of
skill and training were eased.

One of the main sources of relief labour proved to be the
womenfolk of the locality, the 'village women' as they were
officially described in distinction from the 'industrial
women' of the urban working classes. The villagers had a
number of advantages from the farmer's point of view.
They were familiar with the local farming, and might well
have done some work before, in the dairy perhaps, or help-
ing in the harvest field. One of their drawbacks was that
the many with families to look after were not available for
full-time work. The extent of part-time and casual work
makes it difficult to compute the contribution of the village
women. The best estimates show that by 1918 there were
somewhat more than a quarter of a million women engaged
in farm work in one way or another. After allowing for the
numbers normally working in peacetime, agriculture had
an addition to its work force equivalent to about 30,000
full-time male labourers.[8] That made the contribution of
the village women second only to the army as a source of
wartime labour. In November 1918 there were 84,000
soldiers at work on farms in England and Wales. There
were also about 30,000 prisoners of war engaged in farm
work, while the Women's Land Army, the corps of mainly
middle-class women, reached its maximum strength of
16,000 in September 1918.

Government policy and organisation were responsible
for much of the supply of substitute labour during the war.
The government was directly responsible for deciding how
many soldiers and prisoners could be made available for
farm work. The government organised the Women's Land
Army in 1916 as a more effective, better-trained substitute
for the efforts of a number of entirely voluntary organisations that had attempted to recruit educated women to
work in agriculture. The government did not actually

organise the recruitment of village women, although indirectly it was perhaps responsible for an increase in the numbers going to work in 1917 and 1918 as rapid inflation eroded the value of the allowances paid to servicemen's families. As the government's policy towards agriculture generally took a firmer turn from the end of 1916, so the management of the supply of labour also was better directed. The plans for the harvest of 1918, which assumed that 3 million acres of pasture in the United Kingdom would be added to the tilled land, envisaged large-scale deployment of additional manpower into agriculture. A further 80,000 servicemen were to be released for farm work, on top of the 40,000 already so employed. The Women's Land Army was expected to reach a strength of 25,000. The government was also planning to make extra horse-power available: 60,000 horses on loan from the army, and 5,000 tractors were to be bought, in addition to 500 already acquired and sixty-five ploughing sets on order.[9] In the event the soldiers and Women's Land Army members at work on the land were not as numerous as planned. A good many of the tractors and steam ploughs were delivered too late to make a great contribution to the war effort. But the government's direction had ensured a massive increase in the labour made available to farming during 1917 and 1918. Only about 17,000 soldiers were employed on United Kingdom farms during the summer of 1916. By March 1917 the number had already more than doubled, to 36,000. Not only that, but the arrangements for the supply and training of servicemen for agricultural work were being made more efficient.

The government's energies in directing the supply of substitute farm labour were but a small part of a general policy to increase the production of food at home. Left to themselves, farmers were open to the temptation not to worry unduly about maintaining production, but instead simply to leave rising prices to bring in the profits. That was the easy way round the difficulties with supplies of feed, fertiliser and labour. To some extent it is what farmers did, as is apparent from their reaction to the notion of increasing the acreage ploughed for cereals. For the government, increased production of cereals and of potatoes was the key to ensuring adequate supplies of food through the war. An acre of land growing these crops could produce more food for direct human consumption than could the acre devoted to feeding livestock. Ministers in 1914 and 1915 therefore expected rising cereal prices to be the cue for farmers to plough up grass to sow with wheat. They also told farmers it was their national duty to do so.

The rise in prices on the outbreak of war came in time for farmers to respond by sowing an additional 363,000 acres of wheat during the autumn of 1914. Yet, despite all the talk during the past fifteen to twenty years of farmers just waiting for higher prices for them to turn back to arable, very little of the extra acreage of wheat came from grassland. Temporary grass was down by only 20,000 acres when the census was taken the following June, and permanent pasture by 29,000 acres. Instead, most of wheat's increase came at the expense of barley. It was the same the following year, except that the process was reversed. Difficult conditions in the autumn of 1915 had restricted sowings of wheat, and land went back to barley the following spring. Again, there was but a slight fall in the acreage of both temporary and permanent grass in the June 1916 returns.

Thirty years previously farmers had resisted sowing arable land down to grass because they expected the fall in cereal prices to be short-lived. Now they resisted ploughing up grass on the fairly reasonable expectation that war was not going to last for too many years. They would argue that the land they were being asked to plough was quite unsuitable, disregarding the fact that most of the fields in question had grown wheat in the 1870s. Restrictions imposed on

67

ploughing up pasture by tenancy agreements were often cited, and Lord Ernle in government accepted that it was a problem. A weightier, if little acknowledged, reason behind such arguments on the surface was that farmers had become rather attached to grassland farming. The adaptation to the regime of low prices during the 1880s and 1890s had produced a balance in land use and methods that had been earning reasonable returns during the years immediately before the war. There was little incentive for farmers to change now. To do so required capital, which the farmer was quite likely short of. It was also likely to add a disproportionate amount to his costs, so that he would get better returns by continuing with his existing methods.

This, of course, did nothing to meet the government's desire for increased food production. Agricultural production in 1915 maintained the totals of 1914 and the immediate pre-war years, though with a slight shift from livestock to cereals and potatoes. Nineteen-sixteen, though, was a poor year, with total output about 11 per cent below that of 1915.[10] The harvest was bad. In only two years since 1900 had the yield of wheat been lower, and barley and potatoes were well below average. Less meat and milk had been produced as livestock farmers had run into difficulties with the supply of feedstuffs. This came at a time when the prospects for imports were bleak. So far, imports, especially of cereals, had been maintained remarkably well, despite the competing claims on shipping for moving men and munitions, and the losses of ships (table 7). Supplies of wheat from Russia had been almost completely cut off, and less was available from Australia, but these losses had been more than made good by the United States, Canada and Argentina.[11] Looking forward in the autumn of 1916, however, it seemed that such good fortune was unlikely to continue. Harvests around the world were poor. The wheat crop of the United States was 38 per cent less than the good harvest of 1915; results from

Table 7 Imports of cereals and meat into the United
Kingdom, 1914–16 ('000 cwt)

	1914	1915	1916
Wheat and flour	117,899	103,226	113,904
Barley	16,044	12,292	15,819
Oats	14,157	15,640	12,503
Beef	9,678	10,441	8,734
Mutton	5,261	4,767	3,680

Source. Agricultural Statistics, 1919.

Argentina were down by 58 per cent. Added to that was a
renewed threat to shipping from unrestricted German
submarine attacks, after nearly two years of restraint in
deference to neutral countries. When it was launched in
the spring of 1917 the German campaign quickly brought
results. By April losses of Allied shipping were 875,000
tons per month, nearly three times what it had been the
previous autumn.

It was against this background that the new government
of Lloyd George decided to launch a policy of increasing the
production of food at home. The idea was not entirely new.
In June of 1915 the government had appointed a committee under the chairmanship of Viscount Milner to
consider what action might be taken to maintain and
increase the production of food in England and Wales. Lord
Milner and several of his committee were strongly of the
opinion that the country's farms were generally underpro-
ductive. There could be extensive conversion of pasture to
arable in order to increase production of corn without, they
argued, impairing at all the ability to maintain the output
of meat and dairy produce. But the operation of the market
was not enough to bring about this desirable change.
Despite the effect of the Great Depression in bringing
about a more businesslike approach to farming, there was,
in the opinion of Lord Milner and his colleagues, still too

69

much inefficiency. In evidence they could cite the current uneconomic rents, keeping the farmers' costs down and encouraging farmers to do nothing but pocket the extra profit high wartime prices were bringing. The government, therefore, should take positive action to encourage, even force, farmers to become more efficient. The principal means towards this end recommended by the Milner Committee was a guaranteed minimum price for wheat as a promise that the farmer would get a return from the extra costs involved in ploughing up his pasture for corn.[12]

When the Milner Committee made its report in October 1915 a good harvest had just been gathered in, reports were of bumper crops in America, and the threat of submarine attacks was under control. The government, with plenty of other pressing concerns, decided not to take on the substantial financial commitment which guaranteed prices implied. They did, however, adopt one of the committee's recommendations, the setting up of War Agricultural Committees for each county, responsible for organising the supply of farm labour, reporting to the Board of Agriculture any difficulties in the supply of fertilisers, feeds and implements, and for promoting the cause of greater food production.

In the new government of Lloyd George, formed in late 1916 as the management of the war seemed to be heading for disaster, R. E. Prothero, better known perhaps as Lord Ernle, author of *English Farming Past and Present,* took over as President of the Board of Agriculture. He had been a member of Lord Milner's committee, and fully supported its views and recommendations, which he now proceeded to put into practice, adopting as his battle cry in his first memorandum to the War Agricultural Committees the slogan 'Back to the seventies'. This slogan applied specifically to the policy of ploughing up grassland, for in other respects the food production campaign had little relation to the agriculture of the 1870s. Besides increasing the extent of arable land with a view to growing more corn and potatoes, the principles of the food production policy were to direct farmers into more efficient practices through a survey of badly cultivated land. The county agricultural committees, now reconstituted as War Agricultural Executive Committees, were to be the Board's representatives in carrying out the policy. They were to act primarily through consultation and exhortation, but were given powers to order the recalcitrant to plough up pasture and to bring land up to a satisfactory standard of cultivation. The exceptionally bad could even be dispossessed on the authority of the committee.

Table 8 Guaranteed prices for wheat and oats, 1917–22 (*per quarter*)

	Wheat	*Oats*
1917	60s	38s 6d
1918–19	55s	32s
1920–22	45s	24s

The Corn Production Act of 1917, which gave legislative effect to the government's policy, also set out the minimum prices the government was to guarantee for six years as an incentive for farmers to increase their arable (table 8). Barley was omitted because of the strength of objections from the temperance movement. In the event the guarantees proved to be nominal, for prices ruled much higher. Markets for all major items of farm produce were controlled by the Ministry of Food, which set maximum prices. Those for the 1917 crop of wheat, for example, were to range from 75s 6d to 76s 6d a quarter, depending on condition, and the Wheat Commission, the government's buyer, nearly always paid close to the maximum. By contrast, part II of the Corn Production Act had more immediate effect. It established that minimum rates of wages were to be paid. They were to be agreed locally through the administration of Agricultural Wages Boards, but a rate of 25s a week for full-time male labourers was to take immediate effect until local rates had been negotiated.

The policy of ploughing up pasture provoked widespread criticism. 'Ignorance and recklessness', records the official historian, were charges levelled against the Agricultural Executive Committees as they sought to find land that could be prolonged. Farmers complained that they were being asked to plough land that was unsuitable, that they were short of the labour, horses, equipment or money to do the job properly. Fortunately for the smooth running of the policy, the committees did achieve reasonable co-operation, as large farmers, despite their scepticism, accepted places on the committees. Compulsory dispossession was kept to a minimum. At the end of 1918 only 125 farms larger than fifty acres were being farmed by the committees, a total of 24,000 acres.[13] The results of the ploughing-up policy are plainly visible in the June agricultural returns. Implementation of the policy came too late to have any but the slightest effect on the 1917 crops. The wheat acreage was almost the same as that of 1916. Ploughing up pastures during the spring was able to add 174,000 acres of oats and 128,000 acres of barley to the 1917 crop. Vigorous application of the policy had more dramatic results in 1918. The area sown to wheat increased by 645,000 acres over 1916, and oats by 695,000 acres. More potatoes also were grown, 206,000 acres of them, an increase of nearly 50 per cent on the 1916 figure. The extent of both permanent and temporary grass, meanwhile, had been diminished, the former by 1,400,000 acres, or about 9 per cent, the latter by 500,000 acres, nearly 20 per cent of the 1916 acreage.

The corn production policy tipped the balance in favour of the arable farmer. Indeed, the process went further than the government intended, for while gross income from cereals doubled from 1916 to 1918, and income from potatoes rose only a little less, meat production in 1918 was lower than it had been two years before. The numbers of cattle in June 1918 were about the same as in 1916, but there had been a loss of nearly 1½ million sheep, 8 per cent of the 1916 total, and the numbers of pigs had been reduced by more than one-fifth. The emphasis on corn was not wholly responsible for these changes. Farmers were short of both feed and skilled labour. An especially poor lambing season in 1918 contributed to the decline in the size of flocks, and a mismanaged piece of price control by the Ministry of Food caused graziers to bring cattle to market early during the autumn of 1917 before the official price was brought down. Dairy farming especially suffered from shortages of feedingstuffs, as a result of which output of milk fell slightly over the course of the war, although the number of dairy cows remained stable.

The harvest of 1918 was a good one. The yields of wheat, oats and potatoes were all among the best since 1900. The new-ploughed grassland confounded the pessimists by returning for the most part full yields, an achievement no doubt helped by the fact that the land ploughed up so far was far from marginal in quality. Bountiful crops and additional acres combined to give figures for arable production well above the abysmal results of 1916. Production of wheat was up by 56 per cent, of oats by 38 per cent and potatoes 68 per cent. These gains were impressive, but they were offset by the losses on livestock production, both of meat and of dairy produce. Total production in 1918 was higher than it had been in 1916, but no better than it was in 1914. Expressed in calorific values, total production of food by United Kingdom agriculture was 21·2 billion calories in 1918 compared with 19·4 billion calories in 1916, but 21·4 billion in 1914.[14] Clearly, farming had fallen short of the aims of the Board of Agriculture in framing the corn production policy. Certainly, food supplies were in a better state than had seemed possible at the end of 1916. The introduction of shipping convoys during 1917 had helped to keep the losses due to submarine attacks lower than they might have been. But it had not stopped imports of food falling, and, with the results from British farming so disappointing, what finally kept the nation fed during the final years of war was the food control policy. By raising the extraction rate in flour milling, by diverting some of the barley and oats which might have fed animals into the baking flour, and by rationing livestock products the Ministry of Food was able to ensure that there was enough to go round, with only a slight drop in quantity or quality.

The failure of the food production policy is really no surprise, for the government was trying to move more quickly than was possible. Mr Prothero's aim of getting back to the 1870s meant that he was trying to reverse the trends of the past forty years in just one. In the face of the special difficulties created by the war, and the unwillingness of farmers to co-operate, to have added as much as he did to the cereal acreage and to have organised an effective supply of irregular labour was in the event as fair an achievement as might be expected.

Notes

1. Royal Society, *The Food Supply of the United Kingdom,* 1916, pp. 3, 17.

2. Peter E. Dewey, 'British farming profits and government policy during the first world war', *Economic History Review,* 2nd series, xxxvii, 1984, pp. 374–8.

3. Central Landowners' Association, *The Rent of Agricultural Land in England and Wales, 1870–1946,* 1949, pp. 31–52.

4. Royal Commission on Agriculture, 1919, Minutes of Evidence, vol. I, appendix, p. 4.

5. Peter E. Dewey, 'Farm Labour in Wartime' (unpublished PhD thesis, University of Reading, 1978), pp. 83–9. Sir William Beveridge, *British Food Control,* 1928, pp. 30, 375.

6. Peter E. Dewey, 'Farm Labour in Wartime' (unpublished PhD thesis, University of Reading, 1978), pp. 69–82. T. H. Middleton,

Food Production in War, 1923, pp. 186–7, 209, 228–9.

7.   Peter E. Dewey, 'Farm Labour in Wartime' (unpublished PhD thesis, University of Reading, 1978), pp. 179–93.

8.   Peter E. Dewey, 'Farm Labour in Wartime' (unpublished PhD thesis, University of Reading, 1978), pp. 276–88.

9.   T. H. Middleton, *Food Production in War,* 1923, pp. 208–9.

10.   Peter E. Dewey, 'Farm Labour in Wartime' (unpublished PhD thesis, University of Reading, 1978), pp. 53–5.

11.   C. Kains-Jackson, 'The Corn Trade', *Journal of the Royal Agricultural Society of England,* lxxvii, 1916, pp. 62–73.

12.   T. H. Middleton, *Food Production in War,* 1923, pp. 120–1. A. F. Cooper, The Transformation of British Agricultural Policy 1912–1936, (unpublished DPhil thesis, University of Oxford, 1980, pp. 31–8.

13.   T. H. Middleton, *Food Production in War,* 1923, pp. 233–4, 289. David Smith, *No Rain in those Clouds,* 1943, pp. 116–17, 120.

14.   Peter E. Dewey, 'Food production and policy in the United Kingdom, 1914–18', *Transactions of the Royal Historical Society,* 5th series, xxx, 1980, pp. 71–89. Dr Dewey uses the former English billion, that is, a million millions.

5 The inter-war depression

The depression of the 1920s and 1930s was primarily an arable one, even more than had been the case in the 1880s and 1890s. Poultry farmers might complain of competition from egg producers from as far away as China; livestock men could grumble about sluggish trade and low prices; but their problems were little compared with those of the arable farmer. Every survey, every report written on agriculture during this period concluded that it was the specifically arable districts that had suffered most. The Lincolnshire wolds were described in the early 1920s as 'an economic white elephant'. Of the Cotswolds, 'No area in the country has suffered more from the effects of the farming depression since the last war', was the conclusion offered in 1939.[1] Heavy clays, where they remained in arable, were also among the worst affected areas, and one of the bigger tasks undertaken by the War Agricultural Executive Committee for Essex after 1939 was the reclamation of the acres that had been allowed to go to ruin during the late 1920s and early 1930s. Farmers in these districts of light or of extremely heavy soil were trapped by the costliness of the cultivation necessary for arable cropping, while the market for cereals was collapsing. Not even the barley which had helped the farmers of the Lincolnshire wolds during the earlier depression of the 1880s could pull them through now, as beer consumption dropped by about 50 per cent between the wars. Farmers cultivating land of more mixed character could hope for some success by turning to live-stock, which offered higher labour productivity and a quicker turnover of capital. In the light arable country those options were restricted.

The onset of renewed depression early in the 1920s fol-lowed quickly after the return of peacetime free markets, both internally and for international trade. As supplies returned to normal the government was able to abandon rationing and the wartime controls over prices and markets. First to go were controls upon meat and fatstock in December 1919, followed by milk and dairy produce in February 1920.

Cereals were last to be freed, in March 1921, in an epi-sode that gained a special notoriety. It went down in farming's folk history as the 'Great Betrayal', the time when the government reneged on a promise to support arable farming, and thereby plunged the industry into deep depression. At first sight that seems to have been what happened, for to throw the markets open the government repealed legislation passed only a year before. Shortly after the war ended a Royal Commission was appointed to enquire into the economic prospects for agriculture in peace time. Among the matters of interest to the commission was the operation of the system of guaranteed prices under the Corn Production Act. Weighty evidence was collected, not least from those, like Sir Daniel Hall, who had been involved in the implementation of the corn production policy, that price support for cereals was in principle a good idea, and was essential if the government wished to retain the expanded arable acreage of the last year of war. The majority of the commission accepted the arguments for a policy of encouraging arable farming, and on the basis of their interim report the Agriculture Act of 1920 was passed, modifying and extending for an indefinite term the guaranteed prices of the 1917 Act. It was this support that the government rather abruptly abandoned in 1921 when it realised how much it was likely to cost the Treasury in deficiency payments should the bumper crops then in prospect around the world come to flood the British market. Possible totals of £12 million to maintain the guarantees for wheat, and £17 million for oats, at a time when public expenditure had to be restrained were enough to persuade the government to repeal that piece of legislation.[2]

By its rapid change of policy in 1920 and 1921 the government was perhaps doing no more than live up to farmers' expectations. They had never expected price support to continue far beyond the end of war. They had resisted ploughing up grass because of that, and already in 1919 and 1920 some were beginning to reseed land as doubts about the prospects of arable farming grew. Not only did farmers not expect government support, in 1920 they did not want it. There was some confusion in farmers' thinking about this question, apparent, for instance, in their evidence to the Royal Commission of 1919.[3] It arose from the fact that during the war two measures had been in operation, the one of price support, the other of price control, and farmers seem not to have realised that these were not one and the same. The high prices ruling during the war and immediately after had meant that the policy of price support had lain dormant. The dominant policy had been price control, whereby the Ministry of Food determined the maximum prices for cereals purchased by the Wheat Commission. Farmers loathed the controls. By the winter of 1920 the farming world was thoroughly exasperated by the fact that despite the activities of the Wheat Commission in controlling the market, prices for a deficient crop were falling, while a main part of farming's costs was fixed by the Wages Board. A furious row developed between the farmers and the government in these months because farmers felt cheated by the Ministry of Food's buying wheat for about 10s a quarter less than the 95s the Prime Minister had promised to maintain. If this was price support, then they wanted to be rid of it. Even if prices were to fall from their present heights, farmers reckoned they would be better off with a free market in corn. When the government offered that freedom by abolishing all controls over markets, minimum prices and the fixing of wages by the Agricultural Wages Boards the decision was met with considerable relief. That was mixed with deep suspicion of the government, and farming's leaders freely reminded Ministers of their breach of faith in repealing the Agriculture Act with immediate effect instead of giving four years' notice as previously promised. But those cries were muted beside the general expressions of pleasure. 'Part I of the [Agriculture] Act is not a farmer's measure,' declared the *Farmer and Stockbreeder's* leader writer, and one of the magazine's contributors from Berkshire summed up common views with 'most of us are pleased rather than otherwise, as we have all had our fill of control'.[4] It was not until the fall in prices made 95s a quarter but a pipe dream that farmers began to look back and turn the government's betrayal of 1921 into an article of faith.

Free markets were bound to bring prices down from the artificial heights reached during the final years of war. Overseas trade was quickly restored, bringing imports back to their pre-war volumes. Prices fell quickly. Farmers were already changing their tune on wheat by the end of 1921 and complaining that low prices would force them to reduce sowings. Wool prices had fallen dramatically after controls were lifted. In July 1921 prices of Lincoln wool were but one-third, and of Southdown just over a quarter, of what they had been twelve months previously. On the whole, however, the effects of the return to peace were not too drastic. Most farm products lost between a third and a half of their prices of 1918–20 within a couple of years. But that still left prices higher than they had been before the war, and they steadied for the rest of the 1920s before falling with renewed vigour following the international slump in 1929. By the early 1930s the price of wheat had fallen far below the lowest point reached in the 1890s.

Stable prices during the 1920s brought little comfort, especially to arable farmers. Before the war, when wheat was about 7s 6d a hundredweight and barley 7s, George Baylis had been making profits from his vast acreage of Berkshire downland.[5] In the 1920s, with wheat about 12s and barley 11s 6d, he was losing. His was the common experience. The worst years were 1921 to 1923, when prices were falling rapidly. Losses of 10 per cent of capital for two or three years in succession seem to have been common. All were affected, both arable and livestock farmers. The account book of a small farmer in the North Riding shows losses mounting as prices of stock fell all the while he was laying out money on feed. From a healthy balance of £1,670 in 1919 he was down to £163 in less than two years, and steadily selling cows and horses to pay the bills. This man gave up his farm in 1923.[6] So did thousands of others through the 1920s and early 1930s, a turnover far exceeding that of the previous depression in the 1880s and 1890s.

The more stable prices of the mid 1920s stemmed the losses. Things began to look up for a while, such that 1924 saw quite a brisk demand for farms. But it was a somewhat illusory recovery. The losses of 1921–23 had a similar effect to those of 1878–81 in weakening agriculture for several years to come. Profits were possible in the mid 1920s, even in arable farming, but they were slight enough for interest and management charges to wipe them away, certainly not enough to recoup earlier losses.

It is perhaps surprising that, with prices generally higher than they had been before the war, the 1920s should have been a time of such difficulty. The first problem for farmers was that, although the sharp decline in prices had ended, the trend continued downwards. The Ministry of Agriculture's price index for wheat, which stood at 152 in 1924, was down to 130 in 1929. Barley fell from 165 to 125, fat cattle from 153 to 133. Milk was by far the most stable, between 160 and 170 throughout, and it was also among the higher prices. Even better returns could be earned from fruit and vegetables, but they were also extremely volatile, the index for plums diving from 307 in 1924 to 113 in 1926. The base of 100 for all these index numbers was 1911–13.

A second, and bigger problem was that farmers' costs had run out of control. George Baylis had been paying 50s an acre for his tillage operations in 1908–10. Twenty years later that cost had gone up to £4 an acre, a rise bigger than the difference between the prices of cereals over the same period, and enough to destroy the balance of his farming.[7] The main problem was the cost of labour, Baylis reckoned, and so did every other farmer. This had been a matter of some concern since before the war, when the general upturn in the economy had pulled farmworkers' wages slowly upwards. The events of the war had elevated the cost of labour into a major problem. The minimum wage, 25s a week at its introduction in 1917, had been raised by stages until in August 1920 it reached 46s.[8] That was for a working week of forty-eight hours in winter, fifty in summer, considerably less than the sixty hours or so common for summer months before 1914.

If there was one thing the farmers hated more than having the Ministry of Food run the markets it was having the Agricultural Wages Board dictate how much they should pay their men. The arguments about the Agriculture Act and its repeal were as much to do with the farmers' demands that they should have a free hand in the labour market as they were to do with prices. Correspondents filled the pages of the farming press in 1920 and 1921 with claims, slightly contradictory, that on the one hand they could employ many more if they were allowed to pay a free rate of wages, and on the other that wages must come down to match the trend of prices. Repeal of the Agriculture Act dissolved the wages boards and gave farmers their free market, but it proved a great disappointment to them. However they tried, they could not get their labour bills down in line with prices. And they did try very hard. Shortly before its abolition in October 1921 the Wages Board was negotiating a reduction of the minimum to 42s a week. Six months later, rates were already down to 32s–33s a week. Regional variations were now much less than had been usual in the nineteenth century, but in some southern counties 30s was being paid. Further reductions brought the national average to about 28s a week by the end of 1922. Farmers had also secured some increase in the basic working week.[9] But a reduction of a third in the rate of wages was still insufficient for the farmers, and, especially in the arable eastern counties, they continued to press for lower wages, down to 25s to 26s for a week to be increased to fifty-three or fifty-four hours.

It caused rancour and bitterness between farmers and their men. The labourers were suffering badly, first because wages were being brought down more quickly than the fall in retail prices, and because wages in industry and for such country workers as railwaymen were reduced little from their wartime peaks. Discontent found expression in strikes in a number of places in 1923. The most serious was in Norfolk, a county which had retained a strong body of trade unionism among farm workers since the days of Joseph Arch's union. There had been some strikes there before the war, including one at St Faith's, near Norwich, which took up eight months of 1911. Norfolk was also an arable county where the farmers had felt the effects of falling prices particularly badly. They were already crying out for a return to government support, and it was a commonly held view that they were pressing hard on wages partly to attract ministerial attention to their plight. The strike of 1923 lasted for three weeks in March and April, and was another hard-fought contest. Although they had to back down a little on the question of extending the working week, the farmers generally came out rather well in the terms negotiated to settle the Norfolk strike. But the ill-feeling and national attention which had been aroused helped ensure that the Labour government of 1924 enacted the Agricultural Wages (Regulation) Act. Minimum wages were back, administered through Agricultural Wages Committees, and they stayed, since no subsequent government was inclined to repeal the Act of 1924. The first set of minimum rates established in December 1924 gave a national average for ordinary labourers of about 31s a week, with the range running from 29s in Norfolk to 36s in Lincolnshire and the West Riding. Wages were little altered for the remainder of the 1920s, but they were well above what the farmers had been aiming for since 1921.[10]

All the wage rates so far quoted have been those paid to the ordinary unskilled labourers. A large, and increasing, proportion of the agricultural labour force fell into the various categories of skilled workers, mainly working with animals, who were paid higher rates. A survey of farming in Hertfordshire in 1930 showed that 61 per cent of the labourers were paid at premium rates averaging 39s a week, and only 27 per cent were paid at the ordinary labourer's wage of 31s. The other 12 per cent were part-timers and boys not long left school who were paid less than the standard rate.[11] The persistence of high rates of pay pushed the farmer's bill for labour out of line with other costs and with income. During the late nineteenth-century depression labour commonly took 20–25 per cent of the total expenses. In the 1920s only on the smallest farms relying mainly on family labour was a figure as low as that attained. On other farms labour accounted for 25–30 per cent of expenses, sometimes more. The survey of

Hertfordshire put the proportion as high as 34 per cent as an average for the farms studied, after including a sum for family labour. Set against income things looked even worse, for it was not unusual for nearly half a farm's takings to go out in wages.

One recourse for farmers wishing to bring their labour bill under control was to employ fewer men. Yet the number of farm workers in England and Wales recorded annually in the agricultural statistics fell slowly. During the 1920s the number of full-time employees hardly altered, only a reduction by about a quarter in the number of part-time and casual workers making the grand total change. The 1930s saw slightly greater movement. By 1939 the number of full-time workers had been reduced by a fifth from the total of 1929, and there had been a further cut of just short of a quarter in the number of part-time and casual workers.[12] The slow decline in the number of agricultural labourers is one indication of the continuing undercapitalisation of farming. There were now machines available to assist with most tasks on the farm, offering farmers the chance to reduce their use of labour, but they were not being bought. Gross capital formation in machinery and tractors was low, and falling until 1933, and one of the basic reasons was that farmers did not have the money to spend.[13]

In view of the profits earned during the war, it seems perhaps surprising that farmers should have been so short of funds no more than five or six years later. The deep and rapidly developed slump of 1921–23 took its toll of their capital in just the same way as the bad years of 1878–81 had done. For the remainder of the 1920s they were, as one retired farmer put it, 'staggering from crisis to crisis', bumping along with profits just enough to cover basic charges, certainly not enough to rebuild capital. In the mainly arable eastern counties it was calculated that farm capital had diminished by as much as two-thirds in the ten years from 1921, and that despite all efforts to turn the farming to more remunerative livestock enterprises.[14]

A substantial number of farmers had in any case already sunk their wartime earnings into the purchase of their farms. The opportunity to do so was presented by the numbers of nobility and gentry queueing up to sell off some of their ancestral acres. They had started to sell quite extensively in the few years just before the war, stimulated partly by a political climate hostile to landlords from the time of Lloyd George's 'people's budget', but as much by the low return which rent now represented. So it was that landowners, from the Dukes of Bedford and Sutherland down to small squires, put land, mainly peripheral parts of their estates, on to the market. Together they made up an impressive total – as many as 800,000 acres sold during the five years to 1914. But that was as nothing compared with the massive sales immediately after the war. Something like 6–8 million acres, about a quarter of England, was for sale between 1918 and 1921. Having gone through five years when the price of everything rose enormously, except rent, landowners decided it was time to put their money elsewhere, and to do it quickly while agricultural prices were still high.[15]

The buyers were the farmers, almost exclusively. There were still some men with industrial wealth who fancied setting themselves up as squire and were prepared to buy a village. There were not many of them. Most of the land came to the tenants, either by direct sale from the old owner, or through an intermediate purchaser who hoped to make a quick profit by breaking up an estate. The result was that by 1927 36 per cent of the agricultural land of England and Wales was in owner-occupation, compared with 12 per cent in 1909.[16] The farmers bought to give themselves peace of mind: if the estate was being broken up, then it was best to buy the farm rather than let some unknown take over. That did not make them unwilling buyers. With the widely expressed view that the return of peace would take them back to the quiet profitability of before the war, they could feel that their money was well placed in the farm. They were proved wrong, and the new yeomen found themselves saddled with obligations on mortgages they could not keep, and the banks were not inclined to behave like the landlords, who were now making the 10 per cent remissions and reductions of rents just as they had been doing through the 1880s and 1890s. It was generally agreed that the new owner-occupiers, even if they had managed to cling on to their farms, came out of this period of low prices the worst.

Once again, the reaction of farmers to hard times was to opt for some form of cost less farming. As often as not it was a peasant-like approach, of keeping more or less to established routines and avoiding the spending of money. This was the spirit prevailing among the occupiers of modest farms, of thirty to 200 acres, in south Nottinghamshire. They kept by and large to their old patterns of mixed farming. They avoided buying manufactured feeds and manure, not least because they regarded the delivery charges of the railway company as excessive. Some basic slag was used on the leys, some superphosphate on the roots, but hardly any nitrogen for the wheat. Instead they relied on farmyard manure and peas. They had neither money nor incentive to mechanise.[17] It was this approach that left the nettles to grow in the awkward corners of fields, sent scrub advancing up some of the hillsides of the Berkshire downs and taking over fields on the Essex clays as farmers neglected land that required high cost and effort to cultivate. There was a positive side to this policy for some upland farmers. 'I think we stand bad times here in Wales better than in many parts of England,' wrote one of the principality's agriculturalists, 'because, when prices are low, we simply let land drop out of cultivation, and when they improve we take it back again into a kind of provisional cultivation – that is to say, we clear it of scrub, phosphate it, and in some cases lay down a new ley.' That worked quite well during the 1920s when the farmers were able to take advantage of low prices for feedingstuffs and relatively high prices for sheep and cattle. But the slump from 1929 to 1932 hit the upland farmers hard. The prices of livestock fell heavily, and, working already in hand-to-mouth fashion, they had almost no scope for further retrenchment. Several had to abandon the struggle, leaving land to return to scrub.[18]

The plight of the hill farmers accorded well with the generally held view of agricultural economists that 'profitableness is definitely not associated with lower total costs'.[19] Something more was needed for farmers to achieve satisfactory returns on their capital. Investment to overcome the technical disabilities of marginal land in the hills, or even the not so marginal Essex clays, was one requirement. Everywhere farmers had to look for cost-effectiveness in their husbandry in much the same way as they had done during the process of adaptation during the 1880s and 1890s. With the cost of labour particularly high, effort was concentrated on finding the most productive ways of using it. Much was achieved in this respect. Calculations of labour productivity in United Kingdom agriculture show an improvement of 20·7 per cent between 1920–22 and 1930–34. Many of the gains were lost in the later 1930s, however, so that the increase in productivity over the whole inter-war period came to 9·5 per cent.[20]

For most farmers the best way to improve their finances was to concentrate on livestock. Prices during the 1920s for fat cattle and sheep were not always better than those for cereals. The Ministry of Agriculture's price indexes, based on 1911–13, stood at 141 for fat cattle in 1926, 157 for sheep, but 164 for wheat. By 1928 the balance had tipped in favour of the livestock, and as wheat prices fell sharply into the 1930s those of cattle and sheep fell more gently. When the index for wheat prices reached 76 in 1931 fat cattle still stood at 122 and sheep at 133, leaving no doubt as to the advantage of livestock. Livestock had other advantages. They could turn capital over more quickly. The cost of feeding stock was moderate, as purchased feeds were low in price and use could be made of home-grown crops and grass. Most important, perhaps, was the fact that livestock made more economical use of labour, and therefore with costs more under control there was a reasonable chance of profit.

With livestock farming came a renewed emphasis on pasture. The movement back to grass, which was observed beginning as soon as the war ended, continued steadily through the 1920s. By the early 1930s the extent of permanent grass in England and Wales had almost returned to the 16 million acres reached in 1913–16. The loss of farmland to the towns in the meantime meant that pasture had a slightly larger part of the total in the early 1930s: 62 per cent, as against 59 per cent immediately before World War I. With temporary grass added, 72 per cent of the country's agricultural land was growing grass in the early 1930s. In the upland areas pasture reigned supreme. With 86 per cent of the country's farmland under permanent grass the farmers of Westmorland could muster only forty-five acres of wheat between them in 1931. There were but ten acres of corn of any sort in the 200 acres of arable that remained in Wensleydale on the eve of World War II.[21]

In the lowland zone the proportion of arable was generally much greater. About two-thirds of the land in the eastern counties was arable, though even in that region no more than a quarter of the London clays of Essex were tilled. Land had been sown to grass since the war, recouping that ploughed up, often adding to the total extent of pasture. The 500 acre farm in Hertfordshire of Captain E. T. Morris, who became president of the National Farmers' Union in 1930, had had only sixty acres of pasture in 1914. Since the war another fifty acres had been sown, a large increase for this area, though still leaving more than three-quarters of the farm in tillage. Still, there were echoes of the cries of the 1880s from the journalist who visited the farm when he wrote that 'the economic position continues to deny the use of the land for what is its function in the natural economy of things – wheat growing'.[22]

Such was the economic position that not only did Captain Morris not devote himself so wholeheartedly to wheat as his predecessors, even farming through the Great Depression, had done, but his principal means of livelihood was his breeding herd of Lincoln Red Shorthorn cattle together with flying flocks of sheep. In the balance of his farming Captain Morris was well in line with his fellows. Sixty-eight per cent of gross farm income in the eastern counties was being earned from sales of livestock in 1930–31, according to Cambridge University's researchers. This was despite the predominance of arable land, for the crops grown mainly went to feed animals. The greater the importance of livestock in a farm's economy the greater the chance of profit. The Essex clays, so notorious for depression in the 1880s, were now in a stronger state. The dairying and other livestock enterprises established from those times on were now responsible for 86 per cent of farming income in the district.[23] Only where farmers had kept on with mainly arable farming was there serious distress, and land left uncultivated.

The emphasis on livestock brought about an increase in numbers, if only to make up the losses of the final years of war and the slump immediately following. There were fewer sheep in 1920–23 than at any time since the returns began in 1866. In ten years the 13·5 million recorded for those years had grown by about 30 per cent to 17·6 million. The numbers of cattle were less depleted in the early 1920s, and a rise of only 10 per cent was needed to bring the national herd up to the 6·2 million average for the years 1930–33.

Livestock husbandry underwent great changes, especially in the arable lowland zone. The need to keep costs under control meant that greater use was made of grass feeding. The practice of folding flocks of sheep on arable land declined dramatically, and where it continued there was a tendency to substitute such crops as kale for the labour-intensive roots. The emphasis on grassland meant that wherever arable predominated sheep became less important. While the numbers of sheep generally were rising, the increase was modest in arable East Anglia. By contrast, the practice of keeping sheep on grass spread through the Cotswolds, and numbers in Gloucestershire rose by one and a half times the average. Grassland feeding meant grassland breeds, and the arable types declined. The big long-woolled breeds, after surviving the previous depression, could no longer compete. They matured too slowly into mutton of rather poor quality, and demand for their wool was limited. By 1939 the Cotswold was already a rare breed, with just one flock remaining, and the same was happening to the Lincoln. In their place came the Cheviots, the Leicesters and the Downs, and increasingly a host of crossbreds intended to give early maturity from grass feeding. For the trend towards younger meat, which started at the end of the last century, was continuing. It was what the market demanded, and it suited the farmers, who were able to turn their capital over more quickly by selling one-year lamb instead of two-year mutton. The same pressure for quicker turnover meant that it became unusual for arable farmers to maintain a breeding flock. The flying flock of ewes bought in to drop one crop of lambs, and which was then kept for a few months before both ewes and lambs were sold, became much more popular.

Hill farmers were at a disadvantage when it came to following these trends. In the first place, the upland pastures and rough grazing ground were often better suited to a longer period of fattening, feeding yearling sheep that had been kept over winter on low-lying land. In addition, the crop of lambs from sheep kept on the hills was appreciably less than that obtainable from flocks kept in more clement lowland conditions, and the hill farmer's ability to meet the market for young, lean meat was thereby reduced. Even so, the upland farmers had to follow suit. Three and four-year-old wether mutton was hardly saleable now, and hill farmers were as keen as anyone to speed their turnover. Consequently they were stocking their pastures with ewes and rearing more lambs, which were either over-wintered on low-lying land or even brought on for sale by the end of the summer.[24]

Cattle farming followed the trend of sheep farming away from an arable base. Fattening on the long leys and permanent pastures became an increasingly popular alternative to yard feeding on concentrates and roots. Stall feeding was often used as an adjunct to the grass, useful for finishing off beasts being prepared for market in the autumn or for additional feeding when bringing on baby beef. Cost saving was, of course, the main consideration in opting for keeping cattle on grass. Growing roots was expensive, with considerable labour required in singling, weeding and lifting. They became a most unpopular crop, the acreage devoted to them cut by half between 1920 and 1935. There were further savings to be made in the labour employed in preparing roots and concentrates for the livestock, and in keeping the yards and stalls clean. There was also the consideration that with less corn being grown there was less need for farmyard manure. However, the preference for fattening on grass rearranged the seasonal distribution of supplies and prices in the fatstock trade. The springtime glut brought about as over-wintered beasts were brought for sale was replaced in the 1920s by a rise in supply in the autumn as the pasture season finished. The consequent higher prices in spring, compared with the autumn, meant that by the late 1920s those prepared to incur the costs of winter fattening could gain.[25]

One of the attractions of the Lincoln Red Shorthorn for Captain Morris on his Hertfordshire farm was the breed's flexibility as a dual-purpose animal. His main trade was in beef animals, some sold as stores, others retained to sell fat, but he also kept a small number of cows in the dairy.[26] The desire to produce both meat and milk from the one stock of cattle had always been strong, and the majority of farmers probably continued to favour dual-purpose animals. The trend, though, was firmly against them. The need for increased productivity in both beef and milk production meant that farmers were turning more to breeds that were strong in one or other department only. It was a trend which came hard on breeders in the north of England, who had developed expertise in producing Shorthorn cows that were good for beef and adequate milkers.

The greater pressure for specialisation in cattle came from dairying, which continued to grow at a faster rate than any other aspect of cattle farming. Dairy cows as a proportion of the total national herd moved up from the 40 per cent of the war years to 45 per cent for the years 1931–35. Figures for milk production are at best good estimates. The surveys of agricultural output for 1924–25 and 1930–31 provided the best figures, and from these the annual agricultural statistics extrapolated figures for subsequent years. They will be underestimates, but they are good enough to show the increase of productivity as farmers took more care in maintaining their dairy herds. Milk production in England and Wales increased by some 24 per cent between 1924–25 and 1934–35, while the number of dairy cows went up by 13 per cent. Productivity was reckoned to be increasing by about 2 per cent each year, with the average yield per cow, 416 gallons in 1924–25, rising to 539 gallons ten years later. Already cows yielding 1,000 gallons per lactation were quite common, and 2,000 gallons had lost its novelty value. The first Friesian to yield 3,000 gallons arrived on the scene in 1922. By 1930 there were nine of that breed able to claim such an achievement.[27] The exceptionally high yields were mainly achieved by prize pedigree cows representing the peak of a specialist breeder's work. Raising the general standard on working dairy farms was a matter of the farmers being more meticulous about the stock they kept. They were more prepared to buy in from the specialist breeders, thus getting greater consistency than was likely to result from the mixed bag produced by home breeding. The articles in the farming press from time to time featured men who perhaps had peculiar achievements to their credit but also in one way or another typified the trend. There was Roland Stearn, who kept dairy cows on his arable farm near Stowmarket. He was getting an average yield of 1,200 gallons per cow simply by being selective about the animals he acquired and equally strict about pulling out those that gave low yields. E. G. Barton, who farmed at Saundby in Yorkshire, reckoned that the fourteen pedigree Friesians he kept in 1930 were producing as much milk as the twenty-four run-of-the-mill cows he had had six years previously.[28] He was unusual in opting for a pedigree herd. He was also unusual in choosing the Friesian, which, although winning converts, was not yet threatening the dominance of the Shorthorn as the most popular dairy breed. He was not unusual, however, in achieving increased production as a result of being selective about the cows he kept.

The impetus for raising the productivity of dairy cows, and for keeping to specifically dairy stock rather than dual-purpose animals was the increasing importance of the liquid milk market. Dairying for milk required high and consistent yield, whereas variability could be accepted for cheese and butter production, especially if the quality was good. The attractions of selling milk were obvious, and weighed even more strongly than they had done during the

Great Depression. There was clearly a healthy demand for milk, as evidenced by the fact that, in a period of generally falling prices, milk more consistently held its price. The contract price for liquid milk, 16d per gallon in 1922–23, was still 14¼d in 1927–28. The price of milk joined in the general fall after 1929, but that increased the disparity in its favour, as prices of cereals and meat fell more sharply.[29] The good prices meant that expenditure on increased production was likely to be repaid in profit, while the regular income from milk turned the farmer's capital over quickly. The contracts offered by the large dairy companies provided an incentive to opt for milk. The Milk Marketing Board in the 1930s made the attractions more complete, for its method of paying the producer a standard price regardless of the use to which the milk was put meant that farmers felt they were better-off selling the milk than being put to the trouble of making the butter and cheese.

So it was that almost universally through the dairying districts farmers were producing milk in preference to cheese or butter. It was so in Cheshire, as it was in Somerset. Even in areas previously regarded as too remote to join in the trade farmers were now able to sell their milk liquid. Motor lorries meant that milk could be delivered from distant parts of Wensleydale to the collecting depots at the stations, from where, it was reported in 1930, 50,000 gallons was sent to London each week. The Nestlé company organised motor transport to collect milk supplies for its factories at Hatton and Ashbourne in Derbyshire. This last fact demonstrates the real nature of the change. Production of butter, cheese and cream was certainly not disappearing. It was the reverse, if anything. About a quarter of total milk production in 1925 was used in processing. In 1933–34, the first year of the milk marketing scheme, 27 per cent was manufactured. In such places as Westmorland, Cornwall and west Wales the only part of the dairy farmer's output to reach the milk rounds was that required in local towns and villages. The rest became butter and cheese. The difference now was that the bulk of the farmer's trade was in milk sold to the creameries and factories. He had to accept manufacturing prices, which could be less than half the liquid contract. But by selling milk rather than making cheese he still had as much incentive to take up increases in productivity as had his fellows better placed for the lucrative liquid contracts.[30]

Most of those engaged in dairying were small farmers. Three-quarters of the producers registered with the Milk Marketing Board supplied no more than thirty gallons. The regular cheque for milk was particularly valuable to them, since they often had limited reserves. Selling liquid milk was also important to them because it freed them from the burden of producing butter or cheese. It therefore represented a considerable saving of labour, for it was by keeping labour costs down that farmers were able to maintain the productivity of dairying. In practice for the small farmers that meant relying almost exclusively on the labour of themselves and their families. In a sense that merely concealed the cost of labour, but without the employment of families in this way, observers generally were agreed, dairy farmers would not have been half as strong.

It was the need to employ labour as sparingly and efficiently as possible that led to one of the most remarkable developments in dairying, the open-air, or bail, system of A. J. Hosier. Cows had traditionally been kept out of doors all year round in the West Country. Hosier transformed this principle into a system for the economic management of large-scale dairying. He started his experiments with a herd of eighty cows. By 1927 he had increased the total to 210. The basis of Hosier's system was simple. Cows were to be kept out all year on grass, and were to be milked in the fields rather than go through the time-consuming trek to the farmyard twice a day. One of the first big savings, then, was that most of the buildings usually needed could be dispensed with. There were therefore no maintenance costs, and, more important, the expensive daily labour of cleaning the stalls and replenishing hay and straw was saved. There was no carting of muck out to the fields, since the cows were already there acting as manure carts.

But it was on the milking that the greatest savings were made. Milking machines were used, as indeed they had to be with herds so large, and these were housed in portable milking parlours of Hosier's own design, known as 'bails', which were carted out to the fields. The labour savings he claimed were enormous. His bails designed to milk a herd of sixty cows were operated by two men, where from seven to ten men and boys would have been needed for a similar herd managed by conventional methods. Not the least remarkable part of Hosier's farming was that he occupied 1,000 acres of light downland in Wiltshire.

His methods were greeted with considerable scepticism, but he began to win others over. They were not numerous – 192 farmers, according to a count made in 1940. A third of them farmed in Wiltshire, and nearly all the others in neighbouring counties from Buckinghamshire and Berkshire in the east to Somerset, Dorset and Hampshire to south and west, Gloucestershire to the north. In the main they were in similar circumstances to Hosier, farming light, formerly arable land where buildings were non-existent, unsuitable or too distant for conventional dairying. The scale was quite different, but the bail farming system effected a change comparable with the transformation of Essex agriculture during the previous century in enabling dairy farming to be introduced to areas once thought unsuitable.[31]

There were no parallels in the Great Depression for the rise of pig and poultry keeping from relative neglect to become established branches of livestock farming. The number of pigs kept in England and Wales increased by 51 per cent between 1921 and 1936. Most of that growth came in the 1930s, when prices for both bacon and pork pigs were lower than they had been in the 1920s. But the prices were better than for most farm products, and, encouraged by the prospects of stability under the marketing schemes for bacon and pigs, a number of specialist producers invested heavily in the new types of labour-saving housing for pigs that had recently been introduced.

Although the number of fowls kept had been increasing before the First World War, poultry could still be counted among the neglected branches of farming. In the 1920s that suddenly changed, for in ten years the fowl population of England and Wales doubled, from 30·75 million in 1924 to 61·33 million in 1934. Numbers were reduced during the next few years, as lower prices and foreign competition made their impact, but poultry was firmly established in English agriculture.

The growth of poultry farming was predominantly as a branch of general farming rather than as a specialist enterprise. Estimates in 1932 were that two-thirds of the hens kept on holdings of more than one acre were on general farms.[32] This represented quite a transformation in farmers' attitudes, for their distaste for poultry farming had hitherto been proverbial. Hens in small numbers had been tolerated about the farmyard to provide eggs for the farmhouse, and as a source of pin money for the farmer's wife. Now, however, the farmers themselves were happily managing flocks of hundreds, even thousands, of birds.

What helped them to change their minds was the likelihood of profit, since eggs and poultry were among the products which maintained their prices better than cereals and livestock. The sharp fall in prices which began in 1929 destroyed the relative stability of the 1920s, and brought the Ministry of Agriculture's price index for eggs down from 159 for 1929 to 102 by 1934, and for fowls from 143 to 108. Subject to strong competition from abroad, poultry now had little advantage in price or marketing over the main branches of farming. Poultry farming still had attractions, though, from the flexibility of its management. Hens could be kept, systematically fed, in intensive housing, they could be extensive free-range flocks, or – the choice of the majority – they could be managed on a semi-intensive arrangement between those extremes. Their demands on labour were not extravagant. A modest flock, up to about 400 birds, could usually be kept on a family farm without the need to hire extra hands. Moreover, poultry could be integrated into almost any type of farm management. In Norfolk hens were introduced into the arable farming as a means of converting unsaleable grain into a profitable product, and at the same time providing cheap manure for the wheat fields. A. J. Hosier used poultry as a valuable adjunct to his dairy farming. Again, the manure was regarded as important, except that here it went to improve the pastures. The poultry also provided employment for the under-used parts of the dairy worker's day.[33]

The successful integration of poultry into different farming systems was largely due to the introduction of folding as a method of poultry management. Under this system the hens were kept out in the fields in movable houses of various types, ranging from old buses to specially constructed wooden coops with slatted floors to make cleaning easier. The houses were moved every so often to keep the birds clean, and the distribution of manure even. The poultry were thus an additional rotation crop, more literally so when kept on arable farms as in East Anglia, for there they were usually folded on the leys or such fodder crops as thousand-headed kale. Managed in this way, poultry contributed to the general running of the farm, and produced a cash crop, while requiring a minimum of labour.

Even an old bus fitted out for the hens was a vast improvement on the makeshift accommodation that had been usual before farmers took poultry farming seriously. All the new types of housing were designed for cleanliness, and to save labour both in cleaning and in supplying feed. Along with improved housing and feeding the quality of stock was also raised. Recognised breeds – the Rhode Island Red, White Leghorn, Light Sussex and White Wyandotte – took the place of the mongrel barn-door fowl that used to scratch for food around the farmyard. Crosses were also popular, and during the 1930s sex-linkage crossing became widely accepted as a means of avoiding the burdening of egg producers with unwanted cockerel chicks.

During the 1930s the number and size of specialist poultry businesses, producing mainly eggs, began to increase. The stimulus came with the publication in 1933 of the successful results of experiments in battery housing. The savings in costs offered by this method formed the basis of a number of specialist businesses founded before 1939. At the same time some large egg packing stations and marketing companies were becoming established, able to take the output of the bigger poultry farmers.

Growing vegetables was another activity which offered a fair chance of profit, since prices were consistently at or above the average for all farm crops. Demand for fresh vegetables was growing, and a new market was opening with the rise of canning from an obscure trade with one or two companies in the mid-1920s to a sizeable business turning out about fifty million cans a year by 1930. Farmers with good soil increasingly took to growing field crops of vegetables for human consumption. The acreage of carrots and cauliflowers more than doubled in fifteen years, and the acreage of brussels increased nearly threefold as farmers in places from Gloucestershire to Norfolk entered an area hitherto mainly the preserve of small market garden producers. A few farmers became specialist vegetable growers. The most well known was Arthur Rickwood, who built up a large estate in Cambridgeshire, Norfolk and Suffolk growing vegetables, principally carrots, parsnip and celery. The result of all these developments was an increase of 81 per cent in the production of vegetables between 1923 and 1936.[34]

Fruit production in 1936 was also well above that of 1923, but whereas vegetables had increased steadily, fruit fluctuated wildly from year to year as harvests, and prices, varied enormously. It was a business altogether for the hardier souls, since the losses could occasionally be substantial. The acreage devoted to orchard fruit hardly changed between the wars, while small fruit declined. Yet this was also a branch of agriculture that underwent significant improvements by taking up the results of current research. New strains of fruit were developed, high-yielding and resistant to disease. Chemicals were devised to control some of the worst diseases which could destroy crops. More careful analysis and the application of fertiliser were practised. By 1939 fruit growing was one of the most scientific of agricultural activities, with results being achieved in higher yields.

There remained the possibility of making arable farming pay, even at low prices, by efficient management. The key was believed to be mechanisation, by means of which the expense of labour could be held in check, while full advantage could be taken of cheap artificial fertilisers. This was an approach which represented the logical extension of the principles established by George Baylis, whose farming had foundered on the cost of labour. By the end of the 1920s there was no doubt that the machinery available was technically efficient enough to make mechanised farming feasible, and there were some prepared to take it up. Among them were two brothers, S. E. and J. F. Alley, at South Creake, near Fakenham in Norfolk. The farm at South Creake was 1,100 acres, a hundred of which were in pasture. The Alleys sub-let the pasture, to leave them the 1,000 acres of arable on which they opted for simple monoculture of wheat, sowing two-thirds of the land each year, the remainder being fallowed with catch crops such as lupins and mustard. Power for all the work of cultivation was provided by two 40 h.p. Caterpillar tractors. No horses were kept. At first a binder was used in harvesting, but the Alleys quickly took up the combine harvester, acquiring two Massey-Harris machines with a cut of 12 ft. They also installed a steam-heated grain dryer. The labour employed was just four regular men, with three or four extras at harvest, where previous occupiers of this farm had up to forty men and thirty horses. The Alleys reckoned their system was profitable because the machines increased the productivity of the labour and brought total costs down. One man driving the tractor with a four-furrow plough could cover eleven acres a day at a cost of 6s 7d an acre. Using two 33 row drills, and employing two men, seventy acres could be sown in a day. With average yields of four quarters an acre, and selling the straw as well as the grain, the Alleys reckoned to be defeating the low prices of corn.[35]

Such wholehearted mechanisation of arable farming was unusual. Among others who attracted attention during these years was F. P. Chamberlain, at Crowmarsh, in Oxfordshire. He continued to keep horses, and employed more labour on his 500 acre farm than the Alleys did, though this was, in part at least, because part of the land was devoted to growing fruit. The bulk of the arable work was carried out using mechanical power, in the early 1920s steam tackle, replaced by tractors from 1927. Mr Chamberlain did not go in for monoculture, growing instead oats, clover to sell as hay, and potatoes as well as wheat. He, too, expressed himself satisfied with the financial results of his methods.[36]

There were others who took up mechanisation. A survey of the results of farm mechanisation carried out in 1931–32 by the Institute for Research in Agricultural Engineering noted another four arable farms where these practices had been adopted, together with a few grassland and market garden holdings to which mechanised methods had been applied. Taking the whole range of farming enterprises, it is clear that mechanisation was making slow progress during the 1930s. There were 46,500 tractors in England and Wales recorded in a census taken in 1937. Perhaps 5,000, or even 10,000, might be added to allow for the farmers who failed to make their return to the Ministry, though again some might be taken off to account for those tractors bought perhaps at the end of the war and quickly pushed to the back of the shed, found to be underpowered and unreliable. But, set against the 549,000 horses at work on farms in 1939, the highest possible estimate is diminished in stature. Clearly the optimists of the Agricultural Engineering Research Institute, who reckoned farms of quite modest acreage could be fully mechanised, were yet to see their day dawn.[37]

A look at some of the advantages enjoyed by the Alley brothers gives an indication of why that should have been so. They had an extremely large area of arable land, 1,000 acres, in a region of easy terrain. The fields were large, none less than fifty acres. In such conditions it was possible to keep the tractors in more or less constant work – 3,000 hours in the year for each tractor, the Alleys claimed – and that brought costs down, especially capital and depreciation charges. Not many other farmers had that much work for a tractor to do. In a study carried out by the Oxford Province of the Ministry of Agriculture in 1929–30 costings were based on a tractor's being used for 594 hours a year, little more than a third of what a horse was likely to work. On that basis, there was little inducement for farmers to spend scarce capital on what was still rather expensive equipment. The Alleys spent £3,400 on their tractors, harvester and associated implements – a modest investment, perhaps, for a farm of 1,000 acres, but enough to deter farmers unable to make full use of the equipment. The cost of implements and machinery had in any case been rising at a rate second only to labour. In 1931 machinery and implements were some 65 per cent dearer than they had been in 1911–13, while most other costs except labour were about on a par.[38] The horse, therefore, was still paying its way on the generality of farms with a mixture of work. Certainly that was so for the general, light work. For the heavy continuous field work, such as ploughing, drilling, sweeping hay, or as a replacement for the steam engine to drive the threshing machine, then a little Fordson tractor might come in useful.

For Hosier, another keen exponent of mechanisation, tractors and other machinery were the means to the efficient management of his farms. A tractor kept at work for sixteen hours of the day could get as many as sixty acres ploughed and drilled with oats in just four days. He had to employ two drivers working shifts, and pay them extra to do so. But it meant the crop was in on time, and, he reckoned, constant working in this way was ultimately the most efficient and less costly employment of his labour. This was but one aspect of Hosier's whole approach to farming, which was based on the efficient management of his resources. It was an attitude shared by Chamberlain at Crowmarsh, who declared that the farmer of his day 'should be a chemist and a botanist, but above all he should be an accountant'. This was the approach that farmers were having to take, as more and more theirs became a business rather than an occupation. The numerous surveys carried out by the colleges and universities all point to the same conculsion, that the farmers who came out best in these times were those who managed their businesses the most efficiently, and in particular used the most costly resource, labour, to the best advantage. In all these surveys the range of results from broadly similar farming was enormous, from heavy losses to respectable profits, and always it was those who invested in the best stock and equipment, who did not skimp on such things as purchased fertiliser, and who got the best value from their labour that were in the profitable group. There were various ways by which farmers could make a success of their management. Hosier's was one approach, the Alley brothers represented another extreme. There was also Mr Abbott, farming near Peterborough, who split his operations into the component parts – pigs, poultry, dairying, and sheep and cattle – to be organised more or less independently of each other so that labour could become more specialised, and avoid inefficient switching around.[39] But, however they tackled the problem, the lesson for all farmers was that the cash book and daily ledger were no longer enough. They had to concern themselves as much with such matters as turnover of capital and the productive return on labour.

Notes

1. John Bygott, *Eastern England,* 1923, pp. 171–2. B. J. Fricker, 'The agriculture of Gloucestershire', *Journal of the Bath and West of England Society,* 6th series, xiv, 1939–40, p. 20.

2. Edith H. Whetham, 'The Agriculture Act, 1920, and its repeal – the "great betrayal" ', *Agricultural History Review,* xxii, 1974, pp. 42–9.

3. RC Agriculture 1919, qq. 6249–56, 11788–9, 12334–7.

4. *Farmer and Stockbreeder,* 13, 20 June 1921.

5. For an explanation of prices by weight compared with those previously quoted by the quarter see Appendix.

6. Account book in the possession of Mr Banks of Kilburn, Yorkshire.

7. C. S. Orwin, *Progress in English Farming Systems,* iii, *A Specialist in Arable Farming,* 1930, pp. 19–20.

8. *Agricultural Statistics,* 1921.

9. *Agricultural Statistics,* 1921–1923. *Journal of the Ministry of Agriculture,* xxx, 1923–24, p. 109.

10. *Agricultural Statistics.* Reg Groves, *Sharpen the Sickle,* 1949, pp. 252–3.

11. *An Economic Survey of Hertfordshire Agriculture,* Cambridge University, Department of Agriculture, Farm Economics Branch, Report No. 18, 1931, p. 65.

12. *Agricultural Statistics,* summaries also in *A Century of Agricultural Statistics,* 1968, p. 62.

13. C. H. Feinstein, *Domestic Capital Formation in the United*

Kingdom, 1920–1938, 1965, pp. 70–1.

14. Cambridge University, Farm Economics Branch, Report 19, *An Economic Survey of Agriculture in the Eastern Counties of England,* 1931, p. 72.

15. F. M. L. Thompson, *English Landed Society in the Nineteenth Century,* 1964, pp. 320–33.

16. S. G. Sturmey, 'Owner-farming in England and Wales, 1900–1950', *Manchester School,* xxiii, 1955, pp. 245–68.

17. Ex inf. Joseph Fisher of East Bridgford, Nottinghamshire.

18. Stanley M. Bligh and F. J. Prewett, *Progress in English Farming Systems,* ii, *The Improvement of Upland Grazings,* 1930, p. 20. E. J. T. Collins, *The Economy of Upland Britain: an illustrated review,* 1978, pp. 23–4. A. W. Ashby and J. L. Evans, *The Agriculture of Wales,* 1944.

19. R. McG. Carslaw, 'The agricultural geography of the eastern counties', *Agricultural Progress,* xi, 1934, p. 76.

20. E. M. Ojala, *Agriculture and Economic Progress,* 1952, p. 153.

21. R. T. Fieldhouse, 'Agriculture in Wensleydale from 1600 to the present day', *Northern History,* xvi, 1980, p. 180.

22. *Farmer and Stockbreeder,* 20 January 1930.

23. Cambridge University, Farm Economics Branch, *An Economic Survey of Agriculture in the Eastern Counties of England,* 1931, pp. 26, 28, 42.

24. J. R. Bond, 'Derbyshire farming past and present', *Journal of the Royal Agricultural Society of England,* xciii, 1932, p. 180. R. G. White, 'Farming in North Wales', *Agricultural Progress,* v, 1928, p. 44. A. R. Wannop, 'The agriculture of Northumberland', *Agricultural Progress,* xiii, 1936, pp. 44–5.

25. A. W. Ashby and Thomas Lewis, 'Beef production: seasonal variations in the supplies and prices of fat cattle', *Welsh Journal of Agriculture,* v, 1929, pp. 18–37. A. R. Wannop, 'The agriculture of Northumberland', *Agricultural Progress,* xiii, 1936, pp. 45–6, 49.

26. *Farmer and Stockbreeder,* 20 January 1930.

27. *Agricultural Statistics,* 1934, pp. 44–5. A. W. Ashby, 'The milk marketing scheme', *Agricultural Progress,* xii, 1935, p. 1. *Farmer and Stockbreeder,* 24 February 1930.

28. *Farmer and Stockbreeder,* 7 April 1930, 30 March 1931.

29. *Agricultural Statistics,* 1934. A. W. Ashby, 'The milk marketing scheme', *Agricultural Progress,* xii, 1935, p. 9.

30. W. D. Hay, 'The agriculture of Somerset', *Agricultural Progress,* xiii, 1936, p. 40. R. T. Fieldhouse, 'Agriculture in Wensleydale from 1600 to the present day', *Northern History,* xvi, 1980, p. 180. H. G. Robinson, 'Dairying in Derbyshire, Leicestershire and Nottinghamshire', *Journal of the British Dairy Farmers' Association,* xlix,

1937, p. 33. *Agricultural Output of England and Wales* (Cmd. 2815, 1927). *Farmer and Stockbreeder,* 12 May 1930. F. J. Prewett, *Problems of Milk Distribution,* 1932, pp. 12–15. A. W. Ashby, 'The milk marketing scheme', *Agricultural Progress,* xii, 1935, p. 11.

31. A. J. and F. H. Hosier, *Hosier's Farming System,* 1951, pp. 10–13, 24–9. C. S. Orwin, *Progress in English Farming Systems,* v, *A pioneer of progress in farm management,* 1931. R. N. Dixey, *Open Air Dairy Farming,* 1942.

32. *Farmer and Stockbreeder,* 1 February 1932.

33. H. H. Duckett, 'Farm poultry keeping', *Agricultural Progress,* xiii, 1936, pp. 137–41. D. H. Dinsdale, 'A survey of the poultry industry in the north of England', *Agricultural Progress,* xii, 1935, pp. 152–63. A. J. and F. H. Hosier, *Hosier's Farming System,* 1951, pp. 45–9. *Farmer and Stockbreeder,* 2 February 1931, 1 February 1932.

34. O. J. Beilby, 'Changes in agricultural production in England and Wales', *Journal of the Royal Agricultural Society of England,* c, 1939–40, p. 68. Edith H. Whetham, *The Agrarian History of England and Wales,* viii, 1914–1939, 1978, p. 285. *Farmer and Stockbreeder,* 24 February 1930.

35. *Farmer and Stockbreeder,* 4 May, 31 August 1931. H. G. Robinson, 'Notable farming enterprises. Messrs S. E. and J. F. Alley's mechanised farming', *Journal of the Royal Agricultural Society of England,* xciii, 1932, pp. 157–65.

36. C. S. Orwin, *Progress in English Farming Systems,* iv, *Another Departure in Plough Farming,* 1930.

37. J. E. Newman, 'Farm mechanization', *Agricultural Progress,* ix, 1932, pp. 124–35. E. J. T. Collins, 'The Agricultural Tractor in Britain, 1900–40', typescript of paper delivered to the eighth International Economic History Congress, Budapest, 1982.

38. E. J. T. Collins, 'The Agricultural tractor in Britain, 1900–40', pp. 11–12. Cambridge University, Farm Economics Branch, Report 19, *An Economic Survey of Agriculture in the Eastern Counties of England,* 1931, p. 9.

39. A. Bridges and E. L. Jones, *Progress in English Farming Systems,* vii, *The Flexibility of Farming,* 1933, pp. 26 ff.

6 The international crisis and government intervention

In October 1929 the collapse of the American stock market ushered in an economic slump of unprecedented severity. Its ramifications were world-wide, and spread from industry and commerce to agriculture. The world market price for wheat fell by a half between 1929 and 1931, barley by even more, and beef by about 30 per cent. As a major food importing nation, Britain could not help but be affected, and prices, already weak and beginning to fall sharply some time before the disasters to the world economy, were now quite undermined (table 9). As usual, wheat took pride of place. Its official average price for 1934 was but 4s 10d a hundredweight, lower even than the depths reached during the 1890s.

Foreign competition became more intense than ever before. There were large surpluses of most agricultural products on the world markets, and Britain as a major importer of food, and with an open market, was bound to attract goods offered at prices well below the cost of producing them in this country. In not a few instances the exporters had been paid bounties so that the price at which they could sell was below the cost of production anywhere. Dumping attracted the most attention when it took place in the cereals markets, and scarcely a week went by in the farming press without some new outrage against fair play

Table 9 Index numbers of the prices of principal farm products, 1929–34 (1911–13 = 100)

	1929	1930	1931	1932	1933	1934
Wheat	130	105	76	78	70	64
Barley	125	100	100	96	100	109
Oats	125	87	88	99	80	88
Cattle, fat	133	133	122	115	101	99
Sheep, fat	157	160	133	97	110	127
Milk	169	161	147	144	150	163
Butter	152	128	111	102	94	87
Cheese, Cheddar	158	130	116	127	111	103
Eggs	159	136	116	109	105	102

Source. Agricultural Statistics.

in international trade being perpetrated by Germany, France, Austria, and especially Russia being given generous coverage. Germany was first in this field, having paid bounties on the export of wheat since the mid-1920s. They had hardly been noticed until the international surpluses built up in 1929. The *Farmer and Stockbreeder* reported with horror that imports of wheat in October 1929 were 72 per cent up on those of the previous October, and from Germany alone there was a 35 per cent increase.[1] Changes in the annual totals for wheat and flour imports were less dramatic. The peak year was 1931, a poor harvest at home, when imports reached 134 million hundredweight, 15·8 per cent above the volume imported in 1928. The figures for 1929 and 1930 were about 10 per cent higher than usual. The persistent dumping countries, such as Russia with wheat and France with flour, gained at the expense of others.

Competition was as severe in other parts of the market, with other suppliers, mainly European, dumping their surpluses. The effects on British imports were sometimes far greater than was the case with wheat. The quantity of oats imported in 1930–31 was 38 per cent greater than it was in 1927–28. Here again Germany and Russia were countries that indulged in subsidised exports, and increased their share of Britain's imports. Several European countries were accused of dumping fruit and vegetables, and imports of some types rose quite sharply. Potatoes, in particular, recorded a nearly threefold increase in a single year, 1931. Butter was another item to be affected as production increased in European countries such as Denmark and Poland, and in the British Dominions, Australia and New Zealand. After being stable through most of the 1920s, imports rose steadily, and by 1934 were two-thirds greater than they had been in 1928.

Once again English farming was suffering heavy losses as a result of its weak position in a competitive world market. Once again it was the arable farmers who were hit the hardest, and the now familiar pattern of response followed as the falling price of wheat diverted yet more acres to other crops, and occasionally in the depths of depression to no crops at all. In 1931 the acreage of wheat in England and Wales reached its lowest recorded total, at 1,197,000 acres. Wheat was scarcely of any moment anywhere save the east-coast counties from Essex to the East Riding. Even there it occupied no more than about 10 per cent of the farmland, with the exception only of Cambridgeshire. Farmers pursuing economies raised the question of their labourers' wages again. They argued that not only did they need the savings but that, with the cost of living falling, a reduction in wage rates would not come unduly hard. It was a case which had to be argued vigorously, for several of the county wages committees were far from keen to reduce the labourer's wage. One by one, however, during 1931 and 1932 the committees were persuaded to settle new minimum rates, which involved either an addition of two or three hours to the basic working week or a cut in the wage, by as much as 3s 6d in Glamorgan, but usually by one or two shillings a week.[2]

But it was not only arable farming that felt the pinch again. International competition and the effect the general economic depression was having on demand were making themselves felt in all sectors of agriculture. Even dairying, so long considered immune from serious trouble, was faced with over-production. In some cheerless quarters there was an undoubted air of 'this was bound to happen'. The prospects of milk surpluses had been aired on and off during the past ten years or so as more and more farmers took up dairy farming and with greater efficiency. Strains had developed in the trade during the 1920s arising from the control of the farmers' market that was held by the handful of large wholesale dairy companies. Serious problems had been staved off by annual agreements as to prices made between representatives of the dairies and the National Farmers' Union. These agreements had settled the price to be paid by the wholesalers for milk to be sold liquid, and a lower price for milk for manufacturing. Even so, the national agreements were by no means comprehensive, and there were many aggrieved dairy farmers forced to accept local contracts at well below the publicised national prices. Now, however, with butter and cheese coming in quantity from the Continent and Dominions, powdered milk from Denmark, the major dairy companies abandoned co-operation with the farmers and forced the contract prices downwards.[3]

With all branches of farming apparently in a state of permanent and ever deepening crisis there were insistent demands for government assistance. Farmers had not kept particularly silent on this score since 1879, but their efforts had gained them little. A series of Agricultural Holdings Acts, intended to give the tenant greater security in his occupation and to ensure that when he left a farm he was paid for any unexhausted improvements, and a measure of

1896 granting partial exemption from local rates, represented the most substantial legislation in favour of farming passed before the Great War. After it, a belated realisation of the benefits that might have come from the Agriculture Act led to calls for government support to be revived, but they fell on deaf ears in Whitehall. There were some exceptions to the policy of *laissez-faire*. Agricultural land was granted complete exemption from local rates, while attempts were made to assist the financing of agricultural development. The first, the Agricultural Credits Act of 1923, tried to put into practice the much canvassed idea of co-operation among farmers. It failed, but was superseded by another Agricultural Credits Act in 1928 which established the Agricultural Mortgage Corporation to make loans at moderate rates of interest for the purchase or improvement of land. A more radical development of government policy was the decision in 1924 to subsidise the beet sugar industry. It was devised as a measure to support an infant processing industry, the subsidies to last for ten years, by which time it was hoped the industry would stand on its own feet. However, the government was also alive to the fact that it was offering a little stability to arable farming in the eastern counties.[4]

The failure of the farmers to gain any more substantial favours from the government was no surprise in view of the free-trade philosophy which retained its dominance of official thinking, and of the attachment to the principle of cheap bread which pervaded the nation's political culture. Subsidies for growing sugar beet could be justified, but on the grounds of relieving rural unemployment rather than assisting agriculture. Subsidies on cereals were politically out of the question. The farmers were well aware of this, and, though they might voice support for such pressure groups as Joseph Chamberlain's fair-trade campaign of 1903, they knew that louder demands for anything that might smack of protection for agriculture would be pointless. Farmers also appreciated that theirs was now a small part of the national economy, and, as the repeal of the Agriculture Act demonstrated, was not likely to carry much weight against budgetary and industrial considerations.

There was no reason for farmers to expect things to be any different in 1929. The government of Ramsay MacDonald remained committed to the orthodoxy of free trade. The farming interest remained weak in political muscle, the National Farmers' Union being treated with politeness rather than deference in Whitehall and Westminster. Farmers' expectations were fulfilled. While tariffs were imposed across Europe British markets remained open to all. However, the resolve of government was less strong than it appeared. The farmers' demands for assistance began to attract attention. Debates and questions on the issue of overseas competition and dumping were raised in Parliament, and the Ministers of Agriculture, even the Prime Minister, expressed sympathy for the farmers. But it needed another financial crisis and a change of government before free trade ceased to be the central part of policy. That came in the autumn of 1931 when Britain was forced to abandon the gold standard, and MacDonald's Labour government was replaced by a coalition in which the Conservatives, whose policy was to bring in protection, had the strongest voice. Soon a variety of measures to assist agriculture were introduced, to be augmented in the years that followed down to the outbreak of war.

The measures in support of agriculture were varied, sometimes complex, but they fell into three main types. They were tariffs and quotas, subsidies, and agricultural reorganisation schemes, principally in marketing. Tariffs were introduced soon after the new government assumed power. The Horticultural Products (Emergency Duties) Act of November 1931 imposed duties on some of the products that had been the subject of the most recent outcries about dumping, notably soft fruit and potatoes. A more comprehensive policy of tariff protection was contained in the Import Duties Act, passed in February of 1932. A general tariff of 10 per cent on the value of all imports was imposed, although some agricultural products – wheat, maize, meat, livestock and wool – were ommitted. This Act remained the principal instrument of British tariff policy, but its conditions were supplemented and modified by a series of trade agreements with individual countries.

The most comprehensive were those resulting from the imperial conference held at Ottawa in 1932. Imperial preference, which had been introduced into the Import Duties Act, was formulated into a firm policy. The Domimions were guaranteed free or preferential entry to the British market for almost all their agricultural produce. Wheat was added to the list of commodities subject to British tariffs, a special duty of 2s a quarter, with exemption, of course, for Empire producers. Duties on such items as butter and cheese were altered in order to give the Dominions the desired preference. The trade in meat and livestock was not comprehensively settled at Ottawa. Britain agreed not to restrict imports from New Zealand and Australia for two years and to impose limits on foreign suppliers. There followed a complex series of negotiations and agreements, principally with Argentina concerning beef, and Denmark over pigs and bacon, as well as further deals with Australia and New Zealand.[5] The outcome was almost always the granting of import concessions by Britain. Some limits were imposed, for instance on frozen beef, a halving of the quota for Danish bacon, and tariffs on imports from the Irish Free State. But these did not amount to the substantial measures for which British farmers hoped.

When it came to subsidising home agriculture the principal measure introduced by the National government was the Wheat Act of 1932. This revived the principle of deficiency payments, which had been used in the legislation of wartime and the Agriculture Act. Farmers were to be guaranteed a 'standard price' of 10s a hundredweight. If the market price fell below the standard, then farmers would have their income made up, paid not out of Exchequer funds but from the proceeds of a levy imposed on wheat flour delivered from the mills. Since imports now accounted for about 85 per cent of wheat consumption this was really a disguised tariff. It was at a fixed rate, though, for the levy–subsidy system was designed to be self-regulating. If prices rose and less was paid out in subsidy, then the levy fell. There was one further proviso. The government limited the payment of subsidy to a 'standard quantity', a total production of wheat in the United Kingdom of 27 million hundredweight. Anything in excess of that amount would not qualify for deficiency payments. The government had hopes of introducing a similar system of levy-subsidy for beef in 1934–35, but that idea foundered on the difficult negotiations with Australia and Argentina over duties and quotas. Instead a conventional subsidy of 5s per live hundredweight for fat cattle was introduced. The subsidy on sugar beet, due to expire after ten years, was renewed for one year in 1934, and made permanent in 1935.[6]

The third part of the government's agricultural policy was the reorganisation of marketing. Agricultural marketing was an issue which had rumbled on since the early years of the Great Depression in the 1880s. A great deal had been said and written over the years about the weaknesses of the English farmer's marketing methods compared with those of the foreigner, who, apparently, always sold goods of a perfect and uniform standard, whereas on the home market there was extreme variability. Time after time English farmers were told they should co-operate with each other to give them greater strength in the market, so enabling them to get the profits which were going to the middlemen. The slump at the end of the 1920s brought these matters back to the surface once more, filling pages of the farming press week after week. Wholesalers and retailers were accused, as they had been in the past, of all sorts of sharp practices involving the sale of cheap, low-quality foreign goods masquerading as English. Foreign butter was being blended with English, it was said, and powdered milk from Denmark was even being reconstituted and sold on the liquid market.[7] Once again there was a clamour for the marketing of farm produce to be improved, to raise the standards of quality, to increase efficiency and profit the farmer. And the government was being expected to take the lead in promoting such changes.

The first move in fact came before the onset of the crisis in international trade. The Agricultural Produce (Grading and Marking) Act of 1928 gave the Ministry of Agriculture power to establish grades of quality, and licensed traders were then authorised to apply the 'National Mark' to produce which met the appropriate standard. Participation in this scheme was entirely voluntary, and, while egg producers and growers of vegetables were keen, there was less enthusiasm, for instance, in the meat trade.[8] By 1930 the National Mark, an outline of England and Wales with the slogan 'Empire Buying Begins at home', was being seen by its supporters as a valuable means of giving greater prominence in the shops to home-produced goods.

The Agricultural Marketing Acts of 1931 and 1933 addressed the oft aired question of the weakness of the farmers as against the strength of the wholesalers and distributors in the market place. The Acts set up a mechanism whereby producers of any agricultural or horticultural product could combine together to 'regulate the market' in that product. If two-thirds of the producers agreed to a proposed marketing scheme it would gain statutory authority, so that even those who had voted against the proposal would have to fall in with its implementation. Hence the legislation was often referred to as introducing compulsory co-operation. There was nothing compulsory, however, about the initiation of the marketing schemes. Although the Minister of Agriculture could appoint a Reorganisation Commission to do the work of drawing up the detailed proposals, it was entirely up to the producers to decide whether they wanted a marketing scheme. Encouraged by the prospect held out by the Act of additional protection for those commodities covered by marketing schemes, those engaged in five different branches of farming voted in favour. As a result the Marketing Boards for potatoes, hops, pigs, bacon and milk were set up.

It might perhaps be difficult to discern a coherent policy uniting all the various pieces of legislation enacted in relation to agriculture: all the various tariffs, trade agreements, subsidies and marketing schemes. Indeed, there were many at the time, and since, who argued that, far from having a coherent policy, the government was adopting expedients as circumstances changed, or, worse, was merely making a token gesture of support to keep the farmers quiet.

The government may have broken the tradition of free trade, but its policy towards agriculture continued to be constrained by the principles upon which that tradition had been founded. They were the promotion of industry and cheap bread. If anything these principles were more important than ever in this time of economic depression, for whatever claims the farmer might make could be capped by the troubles in shipbuilding, engineering or textiles, while with so many out of work any assistance to the farmer that would put food prices up seemed politically disastrous. Agriculture, therefore, had always to take second place to industry in the government's considerations. So it was that in the trade agreements made with the Dominions and foreign countries the question of maintaining export markets for British manufactured goods was more important than protecting the farmer, and the government was prepared to make concessions on the import of food to help the interests of industrial exporters.

Similar considerations deeply influenced the general principle of imperial preference. There were other considerations as well, such as the notion that it would help create bonds of loyalty and unity which would serve Britain well in time of war. There was plain sentiment. But determining Britain's policy was the fact that members of the Empire were important markets for industrial exporters. They were also major suppliers of food to this country, and, therefore, concessions made on tariffs helped keep food prices down. That may have been sound reasoning politically, but for the British farmer it was no comfort at all. With such generous preference offered to some of the main contributors to imported competition in agricultural markets, the tariffs and quotas and trade agreements did little more than divert trade from foreign countries to those in the Empire. The extent of the transfer in trade was demonstrated in an index of food imports, which, based on 1927–29, had risen to 143 for Empire supplies by 1938, while for foreign countries the figure had fallen to 83. Imports of wheat from foreign countries had fallen by about 40 per cent between those years, whereas from the Empire they rose by about 30 per cent. Denmark ceased to be the principal supplier of imported butter as New Zealand and especially Australia both increased their shares of the total.[9]

Protection, then, was a great disappointment to the farmers, as they were apt to remind public and politicians whenever occasion arose. The Agricultural Marketing Acts represented a more positive strand of government policy, the promotion of efficiency and modernisation. A strong body of opinion within the government believed agriculture should be pushed towards becoming a thoroughly efficient industry, and the marketing legislation offering farmers the chance to direct and improve methods of distribution was the principal device put forward to achieve that aim. There were other, smaller measures intended to encourage the modernisation of farming. Tractors were granted exemption from the Road Fund tax as an incentive for farmers to mechanise. A national veterinary service was established to help raise the standards of farm livestock. The Agricultural Research Council was set up as the single body to administer government funding of agricultural science and to review progress. The drawback to these efforts, however, was the fact that the funds available for the research and advisory services were limited.[10]

Limited though they were, the government's actions did have their effects on the way farming developed. In the first place, wheat-growing began to recover. The new wheat subsidy had not long been announced when it was reported in the spring of 1932 that the farmers of Lincolnshire were sowing an increased acreage of wheat.[11] Their efforts added more than 14,000 acres to the total sown the previous year in that county, an increase of about 9 per cent. It was an experience repeated across the country. As might be expected, eastern farmers showed the greatest enthusiasm, Suffolk, for instance, recording an acreage increased by about eighteen per cent. But in western counties, too, there was a noticeable return to wheat, the extra 2,200 acres in Devon and 1,300 in Chester both representing increases of more than 10 per cent. Even in Westmorland and west Wales, where the wheat acreage for a county was the equivalent of two or three fields in Norfolk, a few more acres were sown. For the whole of England and Wales the increased wheat acreage in 1932 was 1,091,000 acres. The following year, with autumn sowings also coming under the regime of the Wheat Act, the total increased by 29 per cent to 1,660,000 acres, and further extensions took the acreage to 1,772,000 by 1935, the highest since 1923. By then production was some 9 million hundredweight above the standard quantity, which curbed the farmers' enthusiasm and brought the acreage down slightly for the next two years.

Much of the increase in the wheat acreage was at the expense of the other cereals, barley and oats, to which tariffs offered no real protection. A depressed beer market and plentiful imports of barley, and imports of feeding grains, especially maize, helped push the acreage of both barley and oats down until 1938. Some of the tariffs did have noticeable effects. The emergency duties on horticultural products encouraged farmers to plant more potatoes, especially in Devon and Cornwall, where they concentrated on the early crops. Sugar beet had ceased to be a rarely grown crop as a result of the subsidy introduced in the 1920s. When the subsidy was announced in 1924 there were 22,000 acres of the crop in England and Wales. Three years later there were 223,000 acres. Norfolk alone accounted for nearly a quarter of that total, and the east-coast counties from north Essex to Lincolnshire together for more than two-thirds. That remained the bias for the cultivation of sugar beet, which became more popular as a result of poor returns generally from arable farming, while the continuance of the subsidy and reorganisation of the processing industry into the single British Sugar Corporation offered reasonable security. Rapid increases in acreage took the total to 396,000 by 1934 before settling down at under 350,000 acres for the rest of the decade. Again, however, any hopes that the subsidy for sugar beet would revive arable farming generally were disappointed. It certainly did help the farmer's finances, and being the most labour-intensive of crops halted a decline in the employment of casual workers in the districts where it was grown. But the land for sugar beet was found mainly by displacing other crops, especially the roots, but to some extent barley and oats. The predominance of pastoral and animal husbandry even in the eastern counties was unaltered.[12]

The most influential, and on the whole successful, part of the government's policy was the restructuring of agricultural marketing. Of the five marketing schemes set up in England and Wales, three were an undoubted success. The other two, pigs and bacon, embarked on an ambitious attempt to operate in a way complementary to one another, yet leaving the way open for producers to sell pork outside the scheme when it suited them. The marketing boards were left with insufficient control over producers. By the time war broke out in 1939 the schemes were in tatters, and the government's suspension of the marketing boards' operations for the duration saved the embarrassment of their being wound up. The other three marketing boards, by contrast, had thorough control over their producer members. The Hops Marketing Board, with a small, easily identifiable market in the brewers, set out to bring supply in line with demand by limiting the acreage of hops. So effective was the Board's work in getting prices to rise that within a couple of years it was being accused of abusing monopoly powers, and it found it politic to allow prices to fall a little. The Potato Marketing Board adopted similar measures in an attempt not so much to raise prices generally as to smooth out the enormous fluctuations from year to year, season to season. It, too, sought to control production by licensing and limiting the number of acres growing potatoes. It also laid down the minimum size of potato for sale for human consumption according to the quantity coming on to the market. If the crop was large only the big potatoes went to market, which gave the grower a far better chance of making something on the sale.

By far the most successful marketing scheme was that for milk. The Milk Marketing Board for England and Wales was set up in 1933 as a trading entity. Whereas the potato board exercised its control through licensing and grading, the Milk Marketing Board had a direct hand in the determination of prices. It entered as third party into all contracts negotiated between producers and buyers of milk. In this way it was able to see that the terms agreed did not fall below the Board's declared minimum prices, so preventing the undercutting that had been prevalent when the buyers gained the upper hand in 1929–31. The Board was also able to ensure that contracts for liquid sale and manufacturing milk were clearly differentiated, again to prevent the practice of buying at manufacturing price and then retailing the milk liquid. The sums due under all deals struck were paid to the Board, which, after taking out its administrative expenses, determined a 'pool' price to be paid to each producer. The Board divided the country into eleven administrative regions, and prices were worked out regionally rather than uniformly across the country. Pool prices settled at two to three pence a gallon less than the average wholesale liquid price. For the first few years of the Board's existence they were 11½d–12d a gallon, until late in 1937, when increases in retail and wholesale prices were agreed which added about three-farthings to the average pool price. Farmers who sold their own milk retail, those who made farmhouse cheese and those who produced accredited premium grade A tuberculin-tested milk did not fit into the arrangement for determining contracts and prices. For them the Board approved special licences and levies which ensured that their prices kept in line with the general policy.[13]

The Milk Marketing Board's efforts brought a new stability to milk prices. To the large farmers who had been well placed to gain the lucrative metropolitan milk contracts the marketing scheme was a disappointment, since they could have bettered the pool price if left to their own devices. But for those in more remote districts, who previously had been left to the vagaries of small liquid contracts and manufacturing sales, the scheme was a great advantage, often a godsend. For many a small farmer who perhaps had been struggling through the past five or ten years the regular trade and reasonable price guaranteed through the Milk Marketing Board became the means of recovery. More than that, favourable conditions for further expansion of dairy farming were created both by the Board's pricing policies and by its active promotion of milk in the market place. From the outset the Board took seriously the objective of increasing the consumption of milk, and was soon spending £30,000 a year on advertising in the press and by posters, It promoted the drinking of milk in ways other than as an addition to a cup of tea, actively encouraging the proprietors of milk bars, the first of which opened in 1935.[14]

Dairying expanded almost everywhere; the number of farmers registered with the Milk Marketing Board as wholesale suppliers grew from 80,000 to 102,000 in the first five years of its existence. Producer-retailers also grew in number, from 47,000 to 63,000 in the same few years, while the national dairy herd was expanding through the 1930s at a rate about a third greater than it had in the 1920s. The biggest changes were in the far north, where remoteness was now overcome by the Board's contracts and the motor lorry. In Westmorland the dairy herd expanded by 14 per cent between 1933 and 1938 while the average increase for England and Wales was 4 per cent. Cumberland and Northumberland both recorded increases in the numbers of dairy cattle twice the national average, while in Durham and in the dales and moors of the North Riding the small farmers were turning more to dairying. Dairy farming was by now firmly entrenched as the mainstay of the south-western counties, of much of north-western England also, and was coming to dominate those northern districts. It might still lack the glamour, but after nearly seventy years' expansion dairying was coming to occupy the eminent place in agriculture held before the Great Depression by cereal farming.

From 1932–34 agriculture began to recover. The economy generally was picking up. Prices began to rise. The index of agricultural prices, 107 for 1933, reached 133 in 1937. Wheat rose to 9s 4d a hundredweight and barley to 10s 11d from 7s 11d in 1933. Average prices for fat cattle rose more slightly, by 9 per cent, but there was a 30 per cent increase in fat sheep prices, and potatoes, influenced by the marketing board's policies, gained 72 per cent. Production also recovered, an index of all agricultural output rising from 98 in 1931 to 107 in 1937. Production now was reaching new heights, being some 26 per cent greater than it had been in 1922. It was livestock farming that led the way. The output of livestock products increased 36 per cent during the same years 1922–37, while crop production was down by 13 per cent. The recovery in the 1930s was weaker in arable farming, with production already turning down again from 1935.[15]

The fact that agricultural production had increased by so much led one body of expert opinion, including some of those making the government's preparations for another war, to conclude that farming really was securely founded, had been making successful adaptations to economic circumstances as it had done before during the Great Depression, and was capable of making reasonable profits. There was much truth in all that, yet the process of adaptation was really less successful than during the 1880s and 1890s. The persistent inability to keep the cost of labour under control, the serious undercapitalisation, had left agriculture suffering far worse neglect than had occurred before. There were too many scrub-filled fields and broken drains, and the possibility that the great increase in output had come at the expense of the soil's fertility was another question which exercised the minds of the government's planners for wartime.

Notes

1. *Farmer and Stockbreeder,* 18 November 1929.
2. Reg Groves, *Sharpen the Sickle,* 1948, pp. 220–4.
3. RC Agriculture 1919, q. 1344. *Farmer and Stockbreeder,* 7 April 1930. F. J. Prewett, *Problems of Milk Distribution,* 1932, pp. 15–18. Stanley Baker, *Milk to Market,* 1973, pp. 58–61.
4. Viscount Astor and B. Seebohm Rowntree, *British Agriculture: the Principles of Future Policy,* 1938, pp. 94 ff, 378–81.
5. For the development of these agreements see T. Rooth, 'Trade agreements and the evolution of British agricultural policy in the 1930s', *Agricultural History Review,* xxxiii, 1985, pp. 173–90.
6. J. A. Venn, *The Foundations of Agricultural Economics,* 1933, pp. 401–2. C. S. Orwin, 'The wheat quota', *Agricultural Progress,* xii, 1935, pp. 34–7. T. Rooth, 'Trade agreements and the evolution of British agricultural policy in the 1930s', *Agricultural History Review,* xxxiii, 1985, pp. 182–3.
7. *Farmer and Stockbreeder,* 4 November 1929, 24 February 1930.
8. J. A. Venn, *The Foundations of Agricultural Economics,* 1933, pp. 296, 311–12. Edith H. Whetham, *The Agrarian History of England and Wales,* viii, *1914–1939,* 1978, pp. 222–3.
9. Michael Tracy, *Agriculture in Western Europe: Challenge and Response, 1880–1980* (2nd ed. 1982), pp. 169–70.
10. A. F. Cooper, 'The Transformation of British Agricultural Policy 1912–1936' (unpublished DPhil thesis, University of Oxford, 1980), chapters 5, 7. K. A. H. Murray, *Agriculture. History of the Second World War,* 1955, pp. 37–8. Edith H. Whetham, *The Agrarian History of England and Wales,* viii, *1914–1939,* 1978, pp. 273–82. Political and Economic Planning, *Report on Agricultural Research in Great Britain,* 1938, G. W. Cooke (ed.), *Agricultural Research, 1931–1981,* 1981, pp. 21–33.
11. *Farmer and Stockbreeder,* 28 March 1932.
12. Viscount Astor and B. Seebohm Rowntree, *British Agriculture: the Principles of Future Policy,* 1938, pp. 94–106.
13. A. W. Ashby, 'The milk marketing scheme', *Agricultural Progress,* xii, 1935, pp. 7–16. Ministry of Agriculture and Fisheries, *Milk: Report of the Reorganization Commission for Great Britain,* 1936, pp. 7–11, 22–31, 37–9. Edith H. Whetham, *The Agrarian History of England and Wales,* viii, *1914–1939,* 1978, pp. 251–3.
14. Stanley Baker, *Milk to Market,* 1973, pp. 83–90.
15. O. J. Beilby, 'Changes in agricultural production in England and Wales', *Journal of the Royal Agricultural Society of England,* c, 1939–40, pp. 62–73.

7 The Second World War

The day war broke out in September 1939 the Minister of Agriculture told farmers in a broadcast to the nation that they should plough up at least 10 per cent of their grassland to sow with wheat, potatoes, or, where necessary, crops to feed livestock. The lessons learned during the First World War were already being applied, and, besides the declaration of a ploughing-up policy, many of the other features of the food production campaign quickly reappeared. The County War Agricultural Executive Committees were established, the Women's Land Army was reformed. And, while the Ministry of Agriculture took farming into its direct control, the Ministry of Food was established, as before, to oversee the marketing and distribution of food. This time there was to be no waiting two or three years for farmers to respond to market trends and appeals to patriotism.

The government was quick to put its wartime agricultural policy into operation because it was prepared, not by the experience of the Great War alone, but by about three years of work in anticipation of a new war's being declared. Unease at the scale of German rearmament, the formation of the German air force, and Hitler's reintroduction of conscription, all in breach of the Treaty of Versailles, had prompted the Minister of Agriculture in the spring of 1935

125

to set up a committee, jointly with the corresponding departments in Scotland and Northern Ireland, to examine the problem of food production in time of war. The committee presented its report in April 1936, containing a number of general recommendations about the need to increase home production of food, with special emphasis on wheat, potatoes, oats and eggs. From this slightly airy-fairy beginning a number of other studies followed, still conducted by interdepartmental committees, whose reports of January and March 1937 and April 1939 came with a steadily growing sense of urgency, and produced plans from which more definite measures could be enacted.[1]

The first of these was the Agriculture Act, 1937. It set out to reinvigorate arable farming by introducing deficiency payments for barley and oats, and raising the 'standard quantity' for wheat subsidy from 27 million to 36 million hundredweight. As a step towards restoring some of the land's fertility lost through neglect in the successive years of depression, subsidies were granted on agricultural lime and basic slag. The Act also provided for grants towards the improvement of land drainage, and for a major campaign to eradicate animal disease, especially tuberculosis in dairy cows. A national veterinary service was to be set up to lead these efforts. None of all this was overtly a wartime measure. The new Act was in many ways but a logical progression in the policy of subsidy and encouragement to efficiency which had been followed since 1931. Yet, for all that, the intent, following closely the recommendations of the departmental committees, was to bring agriculture, especially arable farming, up to a far better state of productiveness before war might break out rather than wait until afterwards.

The policy was extended by the Agricultural Development Act, passed in May 1939 in expectation of early hostilities. The scope of the deficiency payments on barley and oats was widened to make more growers eligible for subsidy. A special payment of £2 for every acre of permanent pasture ploughed up between 3 May and 30 September 1939 was to be made, an idea which had been proposed in the Ministry in 1938 but its introduction deferred. The Act also offered further grants for drainage, and gave the Minister of Agriculture authority to purchase and store supplies of fertilisers and 3,000 to 5,000 tractors and ancillary equipment.

Meanwhile the administrative machinery for wartime agriculture had been established. The War Agricultural Executive Committees for each county had been constituted as far back as 1936. A list of the principal appointments was drawn up at the same time, but kept secret, even from the appointees themselves, for a while to come. The Ministry of Food was also set up as a department-in-waiting during 1937.

While a great deal had been done, and the government was not entering the war unprepared, there was more that might have been done, certainly more that the Ministry of Agriculture would have liked to have achieved. The biggest shortfall was in the stockpiling of fertilisers, feedingstuffs and equipment. Proposals made in 1936–37 to establish a reserve of three months' supply of feedingstuffs and fertilisers had not been approved by the government, mainly because the cost of buying and storing the materials was thought too high, but also because several departments had more optimistic expectations of the country's ability to maintain imports than were assumed by the Ministry of Agriculture. The modest sum of £400,000 was made available under the Essential Commodities Reserves Act in 1938 for the purchase of fertilisers. Additional powers were granted by the Agricultural Development Act, primarily to buy stocks of phosphate rock. But events were moving too quickly, and war started with little feed or fertiliser in reserve. The same was true of tractors and

127

machinery, procurement of which was barely under way.

The government's plans, drawn up since 1936, relied heavily on the experience of the First World War, which was, after all, the only practical guide available. It was not the most reliable guide, however, since much had happened in the meantime to make conditions in 1939 dissimilar from those of 1914. For one thing, the general state of farming had deteriorated. By 1914 farming had recovered from the worst years of the 1890s well enough to be mildly prosperous, and to offer the government a reasonable foundation upon which to base its policy. In 1939 recovery from the slump of 1929 and after had barely begun, and though farmers might be making profits again, there were still far too many broken drains, unkempt hedges, ragged pastures and fields in a condition which could hardly be described as cultivated. All this meant that a good deal of the efforts of the War Agricultural Executive Committees during the first year or two of war were directed towards repairing some of the ravages and to seeing that capital was spent on restoring lost fertility. Altogether about half a milllion acres were subject to land reclamation schemes organised by the county committees, almost all undertaken during 1940 and 1941. About 6,000 acres of Feltwell Fen in Norfolk, which had been abandoned because farmers could not afford to keep the drains in order, were brought back into cultivation. The East Sussex committee undertook the reclamation of 3,500 acres on the Downs, much of it land earmarked for building plots before the war. In Essex as many as 20,000 acres were taken into the committee's hands to be restored from dereliction or poor cultivation. The most ambitious scheme, though, was in Montgomeryshire, where the committee took on a project devised before the war to plough and grow potatoes on 3,000 acres of mountain land 1,000 ft above sea level.

The changes in the structure of agriculture since 1914 were to cause even more rethinking on the part of government. For the First World War's policy, founded on increased production of bread grains, now had to be adapted to a situation in which agriculture had become overwhelmingly a producer of food from animals. Cereal-growing was the weakest part of farming, even in some of the most arable of counties. All the subsidies paid since the Wheat Act of 1932 had not made cereals any the less subservient part of the agricultural industry. Dairying meanwhile had become a force to be reckoned with. During the First World War it had still been a small enough part of farming almost to be ignored by the policy-makers, and preparations for the next war paid little more attention to it. The need to strike a better balance in priorities between arable and livestock farming quickly became apparent, and resulted in the early part of the war in several adjustments to policy.

For all that could be said of the deficiencies in its preparations for war, government control was able to achieve some dramatic results in the production of food. Output was increased substantially, reaching at its peak in 1943–44 a net value of some 15 per cent greater than the immediate pre-war years (table 10). These efforts also excelled the results of the 1918 harvest, when wartime measures were last in force. Arable crops produced in Great Britain and Northern Ireland were 14·8 million tons greater than they had been in 1918, including an increase of a million tons of cereals and 3·2 million tons of potatoes. In addition British agriculture was producing considerably more milk than it had done in the First World War, which meant that there had been a marked intensification of farming since 1939, and in comparison with 1914–18.

The imbalance between the results of crop production and livestock shown in table 10 indicates clearly the priorities of agricultural policy. Ploughing up grassland was the foundation stone. The 10 per cent of permanent pasture which the Minister of Agriculture had asked in his radio

Table 10 Index numbers of agricultural output in the United Kingdom 1940–45 (1936–37 to 1938–39 = 100)

(a) *Crops*

	Year					
	1940	*1941*	*1942*	*1943*	*1944*	*1945*
Wheat	99	122	155	209	190	132
Barley	144	150	189	215	229	276
Oats	149	167	183	158	152	167
Cereals	132	155	182	195	186	179
Potatoes	131	164	193	202	187	201
Sugar beet	116	118	143	137	119	141
Vegetables	110	122	156	133	144	137
Fodder crops	98	127	133	135	140	132

(b) *Livestock*

	Year (*June–May*)					
	1940–41	*1941–42*	*1942–43*	*1943–44*	*1944–45*	*1945–46*
Milk	90	88	93	96	97	100
Beef and veal	97	73	83	83	92	93
Mutton and lamb	108	89	89	79	72	69
Pigmeat	87	38	35	32	35	38
Eggs	90	75	57	51	54	63

(c) *Agricultural output by value at 1945–46 prices*

	1940–41	1941–42	1942–43	1943–44	1944–45
Gross output	99	92	103	105	102
Net output	106	98	111	115	108

Source. K. A. H. Murray, *Agriculture. History of the Second World War*, 1955, pp. 237, 243.

broadcast to be ploughed up was shortly afterwards set more formally as a target of 2,010,000 acres, of which 1,500,000 should come from England and Wales. Each county was allotted a quota of pasture to be ploughed, with account being taken of the suitability of particular areas for growing crops, and the War Agricultural Executive Committees were given the task of seeing that the target was achieved.

That set the pattern for the whole of the war. Each year a new target was announced for the extent of grassland to be ploughed: 2 million acres in 1940–41 and 1941–42, and another million in 1942–43 (table 11). There was considerable success in meeting these targets. By 1943 the acreage of permanent grass in England and Wales was nearly 5½ million acres less than it had been in 1938, a reduction of 34 per cent. Results came quickly as the subsidy for ploughing up old pasture, announced in the spring of 1939, had already induced some transfer of land during that summer. During the first two years of war the ploughing up of permanent and rotation grasses met the government's targets reasonably well. Nineteen forty-two was less successful. The acreage ploughed up fell well short of the target, 1,186,000 acres in England and Wales, 1,408,000 for the whole of the United Kingdom. Not only that, but the difficulties of maintaining the soil's fertility in these conditions

Table 11 Plough-up targets, 1939–40 to 1942–43 (acres)

	1939–40	1940–41	1941–42	1942–43
England and Wales	1,500,000	1,700,000	1,675,000	800,000
Scotland	260,000	260,000	200,000	60,000
Northern Ireland	250,000	200,000	100,000	100,000
United Kingdom	2,010,000	2,160,000	1,975,000	960,000

Source. K. A. H. Murray, *Agriculture. History of the Second World War*, 1955.

were becoming apparent, and some land was having to be reseeded with clovers and rotation grasses. The extent of temporary grass in England and Wales increased by 346,000 acres in 1942. The pattern was repeated in subsequent years as more land was turned to leys to recover: another 300,000 acres in 1943, and 500,000 acres in each of the next two years. That did not mean the end of the ploughing-up campaign. The need of the military for the ships that might have carried imports of food kept up the pressure on home farming right through 1943 and 1944. Fresh pastures had to be found for the plough. The net decrease in permanent pasture asked for in 1943 was achieved as new ploughings more than matched the amount reseeded. In 1944 the sowing of temporary grass almost cancelled out the old pasture ploughed up, and so farmers fell short of the government's target. But with Allied armies beginning to advance across Europe the peak demand on British farming had passed, and the government was able to live with that failure.

Determining the acreages of pasture to be ploughed up was perhaps the most straightforward part of the food production programme. When it came to deciding what should be grown on the new arable there were too many factors to be taken into account for the First World War's simple emphasis on wheat, potatoes and oats to be repeated. The Minister of Food assessed the possible supplies from overseas and the likelihood of having ships to carry them before announcing how many tons of cereals and potatoes, how many gallons of milk he hoped to have produced from British farms during the coming year. Specific acreages were set for some crops from the beginning of the war, in particular sugar beet, and flax, which the Ministry of Supply was anxious to have grown to meet military needs for fibre in, for instance, the manufacture of parachutes. There were 4,400 acres of flax grown in England and Wales in 1939, which the Ministry immediately asked to be increased by 10,000 acres. The following year an additional 40,000 acres in England and Wales was the aim. Target acreages for potatoes were also announced in most years, but it was not the usual practice with cereals. The Ministry of Agriculture instead laid considerable responsibility on the War Agricultural Executive Committees to persuade farmers in their counties to produce crops that would suit the national interest. It was hoped this would enable local circumstances and the need for fodder crops the better to be taken into consideration. Encouragement was also given to farmers through prices, which were taken under the government's control. The wheat price of 14s 8d a hundredweight in 1941, rising to 16s 3d in 1943, was a great improvement on the five or six shillings prevailing just before the war. The government also ensured that the price of cereals was raised by more than the price of fatstock, further emphasising the priorities in official thinking. By 1943–44 the price index, based on 1936–37 to 1938–39, had reached 192 for cereals, excluding barley, while for fat cattle it was still 154. The extra pressure for home-grown food in the harvest year 1942–43 induced the Ministry to depart from its existing practice and announce targets for all main crops, including an increase of 600,000 acres of wheat and 200,000 acres of barley. There were bound to be disappointments. A wet autumn in 1939 meant that only 14,000 more acres of wheat were sown in England and Wales. However, that loss was more than made up in barley and oats sown the following spring. In subsequent years sowings of wheat showed great increases: 440,000 acres in 1941, 250,000 acres in 1942 and, when the pressure was on in 1943, 980,000 acres. With very good harvests in 1942 and 1943 the government had cause to be pleased at the farmers' efforts.

The biggest problem in managing livestock was the supply of feedingstuffs. Imports of feed grains, oilcakes and other fodder practically vanished as the available shipping space was allocated to cargoes deemed more immediately necessary. From the 6·2 million tons imported annually during the years before the war supplies had dropped to 687,000 tons by 1941–42 and only 156,000 tons two years later. There was not such a sharp loss of by-products from imported wheat and oilseeds, but even so the decline in total supplies of imported feed was 85 per cent, from the 8·7 million tons average before the war to the 1·3 million tons of 1943–44. Meanwhile the ploughing up of grassland deprived the livestock farmer of both pasture and hay. In 1942 the extraction rate for milling wheat was raised from 76 to 85 per cent, so diverting into the loaf brans which normally fed animals, while between January and November 1943 barley and oats were also taken to mix in with the bread flour.

All this raised difficulties for the Ministry of Agriculture, faced as it was with a large livestock industry, ranging from cattle to pigs and poultry, and with the Ministry of Food's insistence on the maintenance of milk supplies. At first the aim was to keep livestock production going for as long as supplies of feed held out, at the same time encouraging the improvement of pastures and the growing of fodder crops as

a substitute for imports. As supplies of feeds began to dimi-
nish attention turned to measures to direct farmers
towards the priorities in production, of milk first, followed
by beef cattle and sheep, with pigs and poultry well down
the list. Fears during 1940 of a drastic fall in milk
production led to proposals that the number of beef cattle
should be reduced by compulsory slaughter so that supplies
of feed could go to the dairy cows. It was a contentious issue
for several months within the Ministries of Food and Agriculture, but was finally dropped in February 1941 in favour
of selective rationing of feedingstuffs, price incentives, and
the continued encouragement of self-sufficiency in fodder.
Ration coupons for feedingstuffs were issued from October
1941 only to dairy farmers, their rations based on their
sales to the Milk Marketing Board, and to specialist pig and
poultry farmers. Holding the price of calves down encouraged farmers to sell their milk rather than use it to fatten
young stock. As the war progressed and the Ministry of
Food continued to stress the need for milk various other
schemes were adopted to stimulate production. The War
Agricultural Executive Committees used their powers to
persuade farmers to cull low-yielding cows and maintain
herds that made best use of the feed ration. The Ministry of
Agriculture provided laboratory services to help farmers
improve the quality of their milk. And there were the
'Victory Churn' contests, more in the nature of a public
relations exercise, with prizes being offered to the counties
showing the greatest increase in sales of milk.

On the whole this policy worked. The figures in table 10
show how production adhered to the government's priorities. There was a particularly large loss of pig meat, as the
number of pigs kept on farm holdings was cut by half
between 1939 and 1945. The sheep population, too, was
reduced by 30 per cent. After the alarms of 1940 and 1941
milk production recovered to 4 per cent less than the pre-
war average by 1943. Considerable progress was made

towards self-sufficiency in feedingstuffs, as the acreages of both oats and barley were greater by between two-thirds and three-quarters by 1943. More roots were grown as well, though the 500,000 acres of turnips and swedes were still a far cry from the acreage of the last war. Good harvests from the fodder crops in 1942 allowed rations of feeds to be eased a little, and though the following year's results were considerably worse the direct predictions of shortages were not fulfilled. Farmers had learned to make better use of their grassland to support a relatively larger head of stock on a reduced area. They were making silage, something to which few had become accustomed hitherto. The Ministry and the county committees encouraged this move by arranging demonstrations of silage making. As more land was sown to leys during the final years of war the number of cattle began to increase, particularly of beef herds, with official blessing as the government started to look ahead to how supplies of meat might stand once the war was over.

It goes without saying that the increases in agricultural production demanded for every year of the war required extra efforts to secure sufficient labour and capital equipment. The Ministry of Agriculture made some attempts at the beginning of the war to retain workers on the land by persuading the government to set the age of reservation for agricultural workers at twenty-one. It had little real effect. The immediate call-up of the Territorial Army, which included about 20,000 farm workers in England and Wales, recruitment of the non-reserved workers, and losses of men to other occupations until direction of labour imposed restrictions, took away an estimated 6 per cent of the male work force by June 1940. Things could not get better, as the war departments continued to press for farming's contribution to the services. The age of reservation was raised to twenty-five in 1941 when an immediate recruitment of 22,000 men from agriculture was demanded. In October 1942 the minimum age for call-up was reduced from eighteen and a half to eighteen. The only concession the services were prepared to make was to postpone calling up additional men until after harvest was over.

Just as in the First World War, therefore, agriculture was to be heavily dependent on a range of alternative workers, a few full-time but most casual. The government had anticipated this by forming the Women's Land Army in June 1939. When the Land Girls came to be deployed they were greeted at first by a good deal of reserve, even hostility, from farmers and their men, who argued that the work of their farms was not the type to be undertaken by women, especially not townswomen.[2] The countrymen would have had to be won over, if only by the sheer need of the labour offered, but the training and organisation of the Women's Land Army made the overcoming of prejudices easier. Once that reserve had worn off, and after the few months in the winter of 1939–40 when severe weather held up work, making it difficult to find places for the girls, the Women's Land Army gained far greater prominence than it had done in the First World War. By August 1941 it had 19,000 members. Twelve months later the number was 52,000, and in August 1943 87,000, which proved to be the limit, as women recruited to war work were henceforward directed to munitions factories. As in the First World War, one of the particular tasks the Land Girls were in demand for was work in the dairy, this being a part of farming with little mechanisation. Those with regular work such as this were assigned to particular farms and found accommodation in cottages or the farmhouse itself. For other jobs, including such field work as singling sugar beet, and special operations such as clearing derelict land, it was found better to employ the women in gangs, organised by the War Agricultural Executive Committees to be sent to farms as required. These girls lived off the farms, mainly in hostels, which it was hoped would be more congenial to those not used to country life.

The only other source of regular labour was prisoners of war. Some Italians arrived in time for the harvest of 1941. By the same time the following year there were some 20,000 prisoners at work in agriculture, the number rising to 50,600 in mid-1944. Again, they were mainly employed in gangs, on the heavy work such as draining, lifting beet and threshing. The rest of the auxiliary labour which farmers could call upon was made up of local part-timers, mainly women, and casual workers brought in for the peak times of harvest. More than 50,000 troops helped gather the harvest of 1942. In addition there were 250,000 schoolchildren, and 100,000 adult volunteers, nearly all people from the towns who came out to specially organised harvest camps to lend their assistance. Local children and adult volunteers also were much employed in the later work of lifting potatoes, with half term usually arranged to suit the needs of this job.

All these sources of labour made a considerable contribution to farming's needs. An index of employment taking into account all sources of labour, full-time, part time and casual, shows that the loss of regular workers to the forces and elsewhere was more than made up (table 12). Without the Women's Land Army, the schoolchildren and the others there is little doubt that agriculture's achievements in the war would have been poor indeed, but they did not make all the difference. For while the index of employment stood at

Table 12 Index of agricultural output in terms of man-years

1937–39	100	1941–42	103
1939–40	99	1942–43	107
1940–41	100	1943–44	108
		1944–45	109

Source. H. T. Williams, 'Changes in the productivity of British agriculture', *Journal of the Agricultural Economics Society*, x, 1954, p. 334.

108 for 1943–44, for net agricultural output it was 125. Two principal factors contributed to the increase in labour productivity thus revealed. In the first place there was sheer hard work and long hours as farmers and their staff made their contribution to the nation's war effort. Farmers who in recent years had devoted their energies mainly to management as a means of making their farming efficient threw themselves into the day-to-day work in the fields. Shift working was more widely practised in order to get more out of each day, though, despite all attempts to get round the problem, blackout regulations restricted plans to keep tractors working into the night. The second, and greater, contributor to agriculture's increased productivity was the fact that farmers were using fertilisers and machinery more than they had done before. Despite the loss of supplies of phosphates and potash normally imported from Germany and France, and the need to ration them for a while, the government managed to increase the availability of fertilisers, especially of nitrogen. Encouraged by subsidised prices and propaganda from the Ministry of Agriculture, farmers who had hardly considered the use of artificials before became converts. By 1943–44 three times as much nitrogen was being used as in 1938–39, twice as much phosphate, and 50 per cent more potash.

The number of tractors in Great Britain, 56,200 in 1939, producing 1,075,000 h.p. rose to 203,400 in 1946, with an output of 3,935,000 h.p. There were probably not many more than a hundred combine harvesters in the country just before the war. In 1942, when the Agricultural Statistics first collected returns of machinery on farms, there were 1,000 in Great Britain, rising to 3,460 in 1946. Potato spinners and diggers increased in number from 37,980 in 1942 to 64,620 in 1946, and milking machines from 29,510 to 48,280, enough to milk about half the nation's cows. Those were some of the most striking changes, but there was substantial expansion too, in the use of all types of equipment, particularly ploughs, harrows, seed drills, balers and other implements that went with tractor power. Transport on and around the farm was also transformed by the use not only of tractors but of lorries and cars as well. Meanwhile the number of horses employed on the farms of Great Britain was falling rapidly: 649,000 in 1939, 520,000 in 1946. It all added up to one of the most rapid changes in the character of farming, putting the country, it was claimed at the time, ahead of the world in mechanisation. There were still large gaps. Almost anything to do with sugar beet, for instance, had to be done by hand, and despite the additional potato diggers it continued to be schoolchildren and other helpers who lifted most of that crop.[3]

The statistics of increased use of machinery make the change seem simple, but again considerable organisation was required from the government and the War Agricultural Executive Committees to ensure that equipment was available. Farmers quickly realised that they were going to need machinery, with the result that demand soon outstripped a supply limited by wartime conditions. The agricultural engineers had much of their capacity diverted to military work. Several of the types of tractor and machinery most needed had in any case to be imported from America, and that meant the Ministry of Agriculture had to fight for shipping space. It was because of these problems that the Ministry and the county committees became involved in the supply and use of machinery. The first steps had been taken before the war when, under the measures of April 1939, the government decided to build up a reserve of 3,000 tractors, together with suitable ploughs. About half the tractors, ordered from Ford in Britain, had been delivered by the time war broke out, with deliveries by then being made at the rate of 100 a day. The government continued to buy large quantities of all types of equipment throughout the war.

The Ministry's purchases were distributed to the War Agricultural Executive Committees, in the first place for use on the reclamation schemes and farms for which they were directly responsible, and secondly to be employed on contract to the area's farmers. This last proved to be one of the most valuable tasks undertaken by the county committees. They were able to make up for shortage of skill in the operation and maintenance of tractors and associated implements. This was especially so in those parts of the country which had been almost exclusively devoted to pastoral husbandry for so long that farmers and labourers were barely equipped to handle arable farming with horses, let alone use tractors. This was so in the dales of Yorkshire, through the Midland counties, even in A. G. Street's Wiltshire.[4]

During the First World War farmers had displayed some reluctance to change their ways to suit the government's food production campaign. There was resistance again in 1939 to government control and the order to plough up grassland. There were many who, having spent the past ten or fifteen years turning themselves into pastoral farmers in order to get some stability into their finances, found the ploughing-up campaign an affront to their efforts and their notions of good husbandry. There were a few landlords, too, who lighted on long-neglected clauses in tenancy agreements and tried to put pressure on farmers and the War Agricultural Executive Committees to curtail the ploughing.[5] The resistance was quickly overcome. For one thing, farmers were not really given any choice in the matter. The powers granted to the county committees to see that farmers worked to standards in line with the government's production policy were extensive, and they were prepared to use them, even down to dispossession. Not many farmers fell foul of that last authority, about 1,500 in all. Numbered among those cases, though, were some which achieved notoriety at the time, with accusations of abuse of power flying at the executive committees, and occasionally some rough handling of police and bailiffs who had to enforce an eviction.

Farmers' resistance to government demands was in any case muted by the fact that, however much they shrank from altering what seemed a satisfactory pattern of husbandry, there was general agreement on the justness of fighting Hitler, to which end farming should play its part. As time went on, moreover, it became increasingly in the farmer's interest to farm in line with the government's needs, for both prices and profits rose, and the gain in both was weighted heavily in favour of those types of farming highest in the government's priorities. Prices followed the pattern familiar in time of war, and rose rapidly. In the first two years agricultural prices rose by 67 per cent, despite government control intended to restrain inflation. Some important farm products, notably barley and oats, were left free of control for the early part of the war, and not unnaturally their prices went up spectacularly. However, the government also had to accept the need to allow the controlled prices to rise substantially, partly to cover increases in farming costs, and also as an earnest of good faith that farmers would be remunerated for the extra they were being asked to produce. Several adjustments were made to prices to bring wheat to 14s 8d a hundredweight in 1941, compared with an average of 7s 9d for the period 1936–38, and fat cattle to 62s 7d per live hundredweight, compared with 43s 10d, the average price for 1939.

The rise in agricultural prices slowed during the second half of the war. In 1945 they were only 14 per cent higher than the point reached in 1941. The need to boost farm incomes had gone, costs were restrained, and the piecemeal approach adopted by the government at first was replaced by a series of comprehensive price reviews which enabled the Ministry to set out clearly the priorities for production. So it was that fat cattle were held to an increase of only 10 per cent for the last three years of war, while wheat's price was raised by 28 per cent. Farmers gained from the rise in prices. Agricultural prices rose considerably higher than either wholesale prices or the prices that made up the cost-of-living index, many of which were held down by government subsidies (table 13). Farmers' costs also rose by less than their prices. Rent was stable, as had been the case in the First World War. Expenditure on feedingstuffs fell. Scarcity alone was enough to ensure that, but the government also held prices down by subsidies introduced in 1940. When the war ended the nation's farmers were spending on feeds an amount less than half the pre-war figure. The other main outlays all increased in amount. The labour bill in United Kingdom farming rose nearly threefold over the six years of war. In June 1940 a national minimum wage was introduced for agricultural workers, set at 48s a week for adult males, well above the 37s 9d average for England and Wales reached on the eve of war in 1939. The national minimum was progressively raised to 60s a week in December 1941, 65s in December 1943 and 75s a week in March 1945. Rates for women, youths and for overtime were also raised more or less in proportion, while a

Table 13 Price index numbers 1939–45 (1936–38 = 100)

	Cost of living	Wholesale prices	Agricultural prices
1939	104	101	103
1940	121	135	143
1941	130	150	172
1942	131	157	183
1943	130	160	186
1944	132	164	190
1945	133	167	196

Source. K. A. H. Murray, *Agriculture. History of the Second World War*, 1955, p. 286.

number of county wages committees set wages locally above the national minimum. Higher rates of wages, the extensive working of overtime, and the need for large numbers of casual workers at peak times all contributed to the greatly increased expenditure on labour. The greater use of machinery involved outgoings on repairs, petrol and depreciation, which increased in total by more than three times. Expenditure on fertilisers increased by a similar magnitude.

All these outlays sent total farm costs up by two-thirds over the course of the war. Yet that was more than compensated by the rise in prices and gains in productivity. The government's price reviews made allowance for increased costs, particularly the changes in wage rates. The reviews underestimated the likely improvements in productivity that would come from increased use of machinery, fertilisers, and management of labour. The result was gain to the farmer, and quite spectacular increases in net farm income, outlined in table 14. The gains were not spread evenly. Not surprisingly, in view of the government's priorities for production, it was the large arable farmer who really did well. Net income per farm for arable farms in England and Wales rose from £285 in 1937–38 to £1,545 in 1943–44. For grass farming types the change was from £196 to £661, in proportionate terms just over half as big a rise as experienced by the arable farmers. Among the poorer cousins were small dairy farmers with little arable on which to grow either cash crops or fodder for the cows, and the hill farmers dependent on grassland sheep which were low in the official order of priorities.

As farmers were quick to point out, the levy of Excess Profits Tax made certain that they did not become bloated with gain. Even so, their gains were great, and not only financially. They had experienced an enforced and rapid recovery from the doldrums of the 1930s. Capital was restored. So, too, was confidence. 'For the first time since I

Table 14 Agricultural income in the United Kingdom
1938–39 to 1944–45 (£ million)

	1938–39	1939–40	1940–41	1941–42	1942–43	1943–44	1944–45
Total receipts[a]	299½	354	459½	499	563½	596½	588
Total farm expenses	242	262	303	326	359½	388½	406½
Net income	55½	112½	188	208	222½	230½	188
Index of net income [b]	97	196	328	363	389	403	329

Notes
[a] Value of output, plus subsidies and miscellaneous
receipts amounting to no more than £12 million in any one
year.
[b] 1937–38 to 1938–39 = 100.
Source. K. A. H. Murray, *Agriculture. History of the Second
World War*, 1955, p. 379.

had been farming the industry was important,' recalled
John Cherrington of these times.[6] It was a common feeling,
bringing out a vigour in farming which had been dormant
now for some three generations. Farmers acquired a taste
for using machines and fertilisers as never before. Moreover it became clear that those changes, and the gains in
productivity and in arable production, were things not
easily to be given up. As the war drew to its close thoughts
both among farmers and in government turned towards
how to avoid a repetition of the calamitous slump that
followed the First World War. Already, in November 1940,
the government, in promising guaranteed wheat prices for
the duration of the war, had made assurances that a
healthy and stable agriculture would be supported beyond
the war. It had been heard before, of course, and was
doubtless greeted with a lot of cynicism, but despite the

uncertainties of the approach of peace it became more and more clear that the stage was set for a major and permanent change in British farming.

Notes

1.   The standard survey of wartime agriculture and policy remains K. A. H. Murray, *Agriculture. History of the Second World War* (1955). It forms the basis of so much of this chapter that to keep giving individual references will become tedious. Several other works have been studied, notably R. J. Hammond, *Food and Agriculture in Britain, 1939–45* (1954), Mancur Olson, *The Economics of the Wartime Shortage* (1963), and the pages of the farming press. I have also benefited from the comments of Sadie Ward, whose book *The Countryside at War* will be published shortly.

2.   Fred Kitchen, *The Farming Front,* 1943, ably portrays a cowman's reaction to the arrival of three Land Army girls.

3.   Edith H. Whetham, 'The mechanisation of British farming, 1910–1945', *Journal of Agricultural Economics,* xxi, 1970, pp. 323–6.

4.   R. T. Fieldhouse, 'Agriculture in Wensleydale from 1600 to the present day', *Northern History,* xvi, 1980, p. 180. A. G. Street, *Hitler's Whistle,* 1943, p. 10.

5.   A. G. Street, *Hitler's Whistle,* 1943, p. 19. John Cherrington, *On the Smell of an Oily Rag,* 1979, p. 99.

6.   John Cherrington, *On the Smell of an Oily Rag,* 1979, p. 99.

Appendix: Prices of corn by measure and weight

For centuries corn was always sold by measure, not by weight, and when the publication of the official returns of prices began in 1771 they were quoted in terms of the imperial quarter. The weight of grain contained in a quarter could vary greatly from harvest to harvest, and place to place, but a number of standard weights became established. The most common were 504 lb to the quarter for wheat, 448 lb for barley and 336 lb for oats, and by the end of the nineteenth century it was not uncommon for corn to be sold by the weighed quarter. A great deal of variation, and confusion, remained, even in official usage. To put an end to this multiplicity the Corn Sales Act, 1921, decreed that, starting in 1923, all transactions in corn must be by the hundredweight. That is not to say that all dealings complied immediately, but henceforth the official returns record prices by the hundredweight. The following table sets out pre-1923 prices by weight and measure to make comparisons easier. The calculations are based on the weights to the quarter quoted above. If some of the other variants are used, then the prices per hundredweight will be up to 5 per cent higher for wheat, 12 per cent higher for barley and 7¾ per cent higher for oats.

Cereal prices per imperial quarter, with equivalent per hundredweight

Year	Wheat per qtr		Wheat per cwt		Barley per qtr		Barley per cwt		Oats per qtr		Oats per cwt	
	s	d	s	d	s	d	s	d	s	d	s	d
1875	45	2	10	0½	38	5	9	7¼	28	8	9	6½
1876	46	2	10	3	35	2	8	9½	26	3	8	9
1877	56	9	12	7¼	39	8	9	11	25	11	8	7½
1878	46	5	10	3¾	40	2	10	0½	24	4	8	1¼
1879	43	10	9	8¾	34	0	8	6	21	9	7	3
1880	44	4	9	10¼	33	1	8	3¼	23	1	7	8¼
1881	45	4	10	0¾	31	11	7	11¾	21	9	7	3
1882	45	1	10	0¼	31	2	7	9½	21	10	7	3¼
1883	41	7	9	2¾	31	10	7	11½	21	5	7	1½
1884	35	8	7	11	30	8	7	8	20	3	6	9
1885	32	10	7	5½	30	1	7	6¼	20	7	6	8¼
1886	31	0	6	10½	26	7	6	7¾	19	0	6	4
1887	32	6	7	2½	25	4	6	4	16	3	5	5
1888	31	10	7	0¾	27	10	6	11½	16	9	5	7
1889	29	9	6	7¼	25	10	6	5½	17	9	5	11
1890	31	11	7	1	28	8	7	2	18	7	6	2¼
1891	37	0	8	2½	28	2	7	0½	20	0	6	8
1892	30	3	6	8½	26	2	6	6½	19	10	6	7¼
1893	26	4	5	10¼	25	7	6	4¾	18	9	6	3
1894	22	10	5	0¾	24	6	6	1½	17	1	5	8¼
1895	23	1	5	1½	21	11	5	5¾	14	6	4	10
1896	26	2	5	9¾	22	11	5	8¾	14	9	4	11
1897	30	2	6	8½	23	6	5	10½	16	11	5	7½
1898	34	0	7	6½	27	2	6	9½	18	5	6	1½
1899	25	8	5	8½	25	7	6	4¾	17	0	5	8
1900	26	11	5	11¾	24	11	6	2¾	17	7	5	10¼
1901	26	9	5	11¼	25	2	6	3½	18	5	6	1½
1902	28	1	6	2¾	25	8	6	5	20	2	6	8½
1903	26	9	5	11¼	22	8	5	8	17	2	5	8½
1904	28	4	6	3½	22	4	5	7	16	4	5	5¼
1905	29	8	6	7	24	4	6	1	17	4	5	9¼
1906	28	3	6	3¼	24	2	6	0½	18	4	6	1¼

Year	Wheat				Barley				Oats			
	per qtr		per cwt		per qtr		per cwt		per qtr		per cwt	
	s	d	s	d	s	d	s	d	s	d	s	d
1907	30	7	6	9½	25	1	6	3¼	18	10	6	3¼
1908	32	0	7	1¼	25	10	6	5½	17	10	5	11¼
1909	36	11	8	2½	26	10	6	8½	18	11	6	3½
1910	31	8	7	0½	23	1	5	9¾	17	4	5	9¼
1911	31	8	7	0½	27	3	6	9¾	18	10	6	3¼
1912	34	9	7	8½	30	8	7	8	21	6	7	2
1913	31	8	7	0½	27	3	6	9¾	19	1	6	4¼
1914	34	11	7	9	27	2	6	9¾	22	11	7	7¾
1915	52	10	11	9¾	37	4	9	4	30	2	10	0¾
1916	58	5	12	4¾	53	6	13	4½	33	5	11	1¾
1917	75	9	16	10	64	9	16	2¼	49	10	16	7¼
1918	72	10	16	2¼	59	0	14	9	49	4	16	5¼
1919	72	11	16	2½	75	9	18	11¼	52	5	17	5¾
1920	80	10	17	11½	89	5	22	4¼	56	10	18	11¼
1921	71	6	15	10½	52	2	13	0½	34	2	11	4¾
1922	47	10	10	7½	40	1	10	0¼	29	1	9	8¼
1923			9	10			9	5			9	7
1924			11	6			13	1			9	9
1925			12	2			11	9			9	9
1926			12	5			10	4			9	0
1927			11	6			11	9			9	0
1928			10	0			11	0			10	5
1929			9	10			9	11			8	10
1930			8	0			7	11			6	2
1931			5	9			7	11			6	3
1932			5	11			7	7			7	0
1933			5	4			7	11			5	7
1934			4	10			8	8			6	3
1935			5	2			7	11			6	8

Select bibliography

Official publications

Agricultural Output of England and Wales 1925 (Cmd. 2815, 1927)
Agricultural Output of England and Wales 1930–1 (Cmd. 4605, 1933)
Agricultural Output of Great Britain 1908 (Cd. 6277, 1912)
Agricultural Returns 1866–1901, thereafter *Agricultural Statistics*
Agricultural Tribunal of Investigation (Cmd. 2145, 1924)
A Century of Agricultural Statistics (1966)
Decline in the Agricultural Population of Great Britain, 1881–1906 (Cd. 3273, 1906)
Reorganisation Commission for Milk, *Reports,* 1933 and 1936
Royal Commissions:
  Depressed Condition of the Agricultural Interest, 1879 (cited as RC Agricultural Interest 1879)
  Agriculture, 1893 (cited as RC Agriculture 1893)
  Agriculture, 1919 (cited as RC Agriculture 1919)

Books and articles

A. W. Ashby, 'The milk marketing scheme', *Agricultural Progress,* xii, 1935, pp. 7–16.
A. W. Ashby and J. L. Evans, *The Agriculture of Wales,* 1944.
Viscount Astor and B. Seebohm Rowntree, *British Agriculture: the Principles of Future Policy,* 1938.
P. J. Atkins, 'The growth of London's railway milk trade c. 1845–1914', *Journal of Transport History,* new series, iv, 1977–8.
Stanley Baker, *Milk to Market,* 1973.
W. E. Bear, 'The future of agricultural competition', *Journal of the*

Royal Agricultural Society of England, lii, 1891, pp. 742–71.

O. J. Beilby, 'Changes in agricultural production in England and Wales', *Journal of the Royal Agricultural Society of England,* c. 1939–40, pp. 62–73.

J. R. Bellerby, *Agriculture and Industry Relative Income,* 1956.

Sir William Beveridge, *British Food Control,* 1928.

Stanley M. Bligh and F. J. Prewett, *Progress in English Farming Systems,* ii, *The improvement of upland grazings,* 1930.

J. R. Bond, 'Derbyshire farming past and present', *Journal of the Royal Agricultural Society of England,* xciii, 1932, pp. 165–89.

Thomas Brassey, 'Agriculture in England and the United States', *Journal of the Royal Statistical Society,* xlii, 1879, pp. 751–64.

A. Bridges and E. L. Jones, *Progress in English Farming Systems,* vii, *The flexibility of farming,* 1933.

John Bygott, *Eastern England,* 1923.

J. Caird, 'Recent experience in laying down land to grass', *Journal of the Royal Agricultural Society of England,* xlix, 1888, pp. 124–56.

J. Caird, 'Fifty years' progress of British agriculture', *Journal of the Royal Agricultural Society of England,* li, 1890, pp. 20–36.

R. McG. Carslaw, 'The agricultural geography of the eastern counties', *Agricultural Progress,* xi, 1934, pp. 70–6.

Central Landowners' Association, *The Rent of Agricultural Land in England and Wales, 1870–1946,* 1949.

Ruth L. Cohen, 'The potato marketing scheme', *Agricultural Progress,* xii, 1935, pp. 17–23.

E. J. T. Collins, *Sickle to Combine,* 1969.

E. J. T. Collins, *A History of the Orsett Estate, 1743–1914,* 1978.

E. J. T. Collins, *The Economy of Upland Britain: an illustrated review,* 1978.

E. J. T. Collins, 'The Agricultural Tractor in Britain, 1900–1940', paper delivered to the 8th International Economic History Congress, Budapest, 1982.

J. T. Coppock, 'Agricultural changes in the Chilterns, 1875–1900', *Agricultural History Review,* ix, 1961, reprinted in P. J. Perry (ed.), *British Agriculture, 1875–1914,* 1973, pp. 56–76.

A. F. Cooper, 'The Transformation of British Agricultural Policy, 1912–1936' (unpublished DPhil thesis, University of Oxford, 1980).

Peter E. Dewey, 'Farm Labour in Wartime' (unpublished PhD thesis, University of Reading, 1978).

Peter E. Dewey, 'Food production and policy in the United Kingdom 1914–1918', *Transactions of the Royal Historical Society,* fifth series, xxx, 1980, pp. 71–89.

Peter E. Dewey, 'British farming profits and government policy during the first world war', *Economic History Review,* second series, xxxvii, 1984, pp. 373–90.

R. N. Dixey, *Open Air Dairy Farming,* 1942.

C. H. Feinstein, *Domestic Capital Formation in the United Kingdom, 1920–1938,* 1965.

R. T. Fieldhouse, 'Agriculture in Wensleydale from 1600 to the present day', *Northern History,* xvi, 1980, pp. 169–95.

John Fisher, 'The economic effect of cattle disease in Britain and its containment, 1850–1900', *Agricultural History,* liv, 1980.

T. W. Fletcher, 'The Great Depression in English agriculture, 1873–1896', *Economic History Review,* second series, viii, 1961–2, reprinted in W. E. Minchinton (ed.), *Essays in Agrarian History,* ii, 1968, pp. 239–56.

T. W. Fletcher, 'Lancashire livestock husbandry during the Great Depression', *Agricultural History Review,* ix, 1961, reprinted in P. J. Perry (ed.), *British Agriculture, 1875–1914,* 1973, pp. 77–108.

A. Wilson Fox, 'Agricultural wages in England during the last half-century', *Journal of the Royal Statistical Society,* lxvi, 1903, reprinted in W. E. Minchinton (ed.), *Essays in Agrarian History,* ii, 1968, pp. 121–98.

B. J. Fricker, 'The agriculture of Gloucestershire', *Journal of the Bath and West of England Society,* sixth series, xiv, 1939–40, pp. 16–21.

R. C. Gaut, *A History of Worcestershire Agriculture,* 1939.

P. A. Graham, *The Revival of English Agriculture,* 1899.

Reg Groves, *Sharpen the Sickle,* 1949.

H. Rider Haggard, *Rural England,* 1902.

Sir Daniel Hall, *A Pilgrimage of British Farming,* 1913.

R. J. Hammond, *Food and Agriculture in Britain, 1939–45,* 1954.

A. J. and F. H. Hosier, *Hosier's Farming System,* 1951.

David Howell, *Land and People in Nineteenth Century Wales,* 1978.

E. L. Jones, 'The changing basis of agricultural prosperity, 1852–1873', *Agricultural History Review,* x, 1962, pp. 102–19.

W. T. Layton and G. Crowther, *An Introduction to the Study of Prices,* second edition, 1935.

Primrose McConnell, 'Experiences of a Scotsman on the Essex clays', *Journal of the Royal Agricultural Society of England,* lii, 1891, pp. 311–25.

Gavin McCrone, *The Economics of Subsidising Agriculture,* 1962.

J. D. Marshall and John K. Walton, *The Lake Counties from 1830 to the mid-twentieth century,* 1981.

J. P. Maxton (ed.), *Regional Types of British Agriculture,* 1936.

T. H. Middleton, *Food Production in War,* 1954.

Milk Marketing Board, *Milk Marketing Scheme: Five Years' Review,*

1933–1938 (n.d.).

K. A. H. Murray, *Agriculture. History of the Second World War,* 1955.

K. A. H. Murray and Ruth L. Cohen, *The Planning of Britain's Food Imports,* 1934.

Alistair Mutch, 'The mechanisation of the harvest in south-west Lancashire, 1850–1914', *Agricultural History Review,* xxix, 1981, pp. 125–32.

E. M. Ojala, *Agriculture and Economic Progress,* 1952.

J. Orr, *Agriculture in Oxfordshire,* 1916.

J. Orr, *Agriculture in Berkshire,* 1918.

C. S. Orwin, *Progress in English Farming Systems,* iii, *A specialist in arable farming,* 1930.

C. S. Orwin, *Progress in English Farming Systems,* iv, *Another departure in plough farming,* 1930.

C. S. Orwin, *Progress in English Farming Systems,* v, *A pioneer of progress in farm management,* 1931.

C. S. Orwin and Edith H. Whetham, *History of British Agriculture, 1846–1914,* 1963.

Richard Perren, *The Meat Trade in Britain, 1840–1914,* 1978.

P. J. Perry, *British Farming in the Great Depression, 1870–1914,* 1974.

E. A. Pratt, *The Transition in Agriculture,* 1906.

Guy Robinson, 'A statistical analysis of agriculture in the Vale of Evesham during the "great agricultural depression" ', *Journal of Historical Geography,* vii, 1981, pp. 37–52.

T. Rooth, 'Trade agreements and the evolution of British agricultural policy in the 1930s', *Agricultural History Review,* xxxiii, 1985, pp. 173–90.

Royal Society, *The Food Supply of the United Kingdom,* 1916.

Vita Sackville-West, *The Women's Land Army,* 1944.

John Sheail, 'Land improvement and reclamation: the experience of the first world war in England and Wales', *Agricultural History Review,* xxiv, 1976, pp. 110–25.

S. G. Sturmey, 'Owner-farming in England and Wales, 1900–1950', *Manchester School,* xxiii, 1955, reprinted in W. E. Minchinton (ed.), *Essays in Agrarian History,* ii, 1968, pp. 281–306.

David Taylor, 'London's milk supply, 1850–1900: a reinterpretation', *Agricultural History,* xlv, 1971, pp. 33–8.

David Taylor, 'The English dairy industry, 1860–1930: the need for a reassessment', *Agricultural History Review,* xxii, 1974, pp. 153–9.

Joan Thirsk and Jean Imray, *Suffolk Farming in the Nineteenth Century,* 1958.

F. M. L. Thompson, 'Agriculture since 1870', *Victoria County*

History, Wiltshire, iv, 1959, pp. 92–114.

F. M. L. Thompson, *English Landed Society in the Nineteenth Century,* 1963.

Michael Tracy, *Agriculture in Western Europe: Challenge and Response, 1880–1980,* second edition, 1982.

J. A. Venn, *The Foundations of Agricultural Economics,* 1933.

A. R. Wannop, 'The agriculture of Northumberland', *Agricultural Progress,* xiii, 1936.

Edith H. Whetham, 'The Agriculture Act, 1920, and its repeal – the "great betrayal" ', *Agricultural History Review,* xxii, 1974, pp. 36–49.

Edith H. Whetham, *The Agrarian History of England and Wales,* viii, *1914–1939,* 1978.

R. G. White, 'Farming in North Wales', *Agricultural Progress,* v, 1928.

Index